Aiming for Overshoot
The Handbook You Need to Overcome a Restrictive Eating Disorder

Helly Barnes

Contents

Foreword

Hey there,

This handbook is written for anyone who is in the process of overcoming a restrictive eating disorder or currently contemplating it.

Aiming for Overshoot, has been written to accompany my first book, *Addicted to Energy Deficit*.

Addicted to Energy Deficit focused on the compelling theory that restrictive eating disorders are a form of addiction and the *drug* your brain is addicted to is your body being in a state of energy deficit. The book dives into this theory, applying neuroscience and research evidence to help you understand the addiction model for eating disorders. In this way, it helps you to develop a deeper insight into what drives a restrictive eating disorder and why they are so hard to overcome.

This handbook doesn't repeat information included in *Addicted to Energy Deficit* unless it's beneficial to clarify a point. But you don't need to have read the first book to benefit from and understand this one. The two books are published separately so that you have the choice of the science and research included in the first, the practical hints and tips of this one or you can absolutely read and benefit from both!

For those of you who haven't read *Addicted to Energy Deficit* or who need a refresher on the information provided within it, some of the key points are given below. A basic understanding of these will help you as you read the coming chapters.

Key Points from *Addicted to Energy Deficit*:

- Restrictive eating disorders are an addiction to your body being in a state of energy deficit (which is your *drug*).

- Behaviours that initially led to energy deficit gave your brain a surge in dopamine and natural opioids which felt amazing. This made your brain seek more of these high rewards and the behaviours then became compulsive and addictive.

- To make the addictive behaviours easier to pursue, your brain wired in deeply embedded neural pathways and networks. This turned them into automatic and compulsive habits.

- Over time, you develop rituals around the compulsive energy deficit-creating behaviours. These rituals become powerful triggers to pursue your drug and in themselves can be compulsive.

- To overcome a restrictive eating disorder, you need to reprogram your brain. There are two parts to this:

  a. **Deep learning**. When you abstain from the old behaviours and stop using the brain networks that drive them, your brain will begin to break down the unused pathways in a process called *unwiring*. As you simultaneously develop new learning and behaviours in pursuit of a healthier life, your brain develops circuits and networks which then embed or *wire in* as new habits.

b. **A dopamine reset**. Years of pursuing highly rewarding behaviours with an addiction such as an eating disorder, leaves your brain in a deep dopamine deficit state. This means that when you are not engaging in eating disorder behaviours, you feel depressed, agitated, anxious and irritable. When you abstain from the eating disorder's pursuit of energy deficit for long enough, your brain will naturally restore your dopamine to a level at which you feel normal again, without needing to use dopamine-seeking behaviours to achieve this calmer state.

- There are two approaches to overcoming a restrictive eating disorder. The first and most effective is abstinence from all behaviours and restrictive eating. The second is a moderation approach.

- When you abstain from all behaviours that pursue or maintain energy deficit and purposefully engage in behaviours to create an energy surplus, aiming for overshoot, you give your brain the best chance to reprogram and your body can fully restore and heal.

- Moderation approaches can be useful in the process but in the long term, they carry more risk of failure or relapse and will make it much harder to fully overcome the eating disorder.

- When you actively pursue behaviours that will create an energy surplus, you will restore energy balance. Until energy balance is achieved you cannot fully overcome the eating disorder because you haven't escaped the state of energy deficit that your brain is addicted to.

- Escaping energy deficit and restoring your body to a state of energy balance makes weight gain unavoidable.

- To restore energy balance, your body needs to fully restore fat and lean tissue stores to genetically determined set point levels that it perceives as minimally necessary. To get both tissue types to your unique set points, your body needs to first gain an overshoot amount of fat. This is necessary to allow full completion of lean tissue restoration. Unless you allow for this fat overshoot, lean tissue repairs will not be fully achieved and your body will remain in a state of energy deficit. The overshoot fat will be lost naturally once lean tissues are fully restored.

- The addiction model to eating disorders sits alongside the evolutionary theory that restrictive eating disorders were once a necessary response to a famine situation. When our nomadic ancestors faced an environment of food scarcity, it was beneficial if they could ignore the limited food that was still available, feel a constant urge to move and fail to notice how emaciated they were. These factors enabled them to migrate with their tribe to a new foraging ground.

- Recent research demonstrates that there are genetic links to eating disorders. Your genetic blueprint can make you susceptible and these genes can be switched on by certain factors.

- The key trigger to *switching on* your genetic vulnerability to develop a restrictive eating disorder is to enter a state of energy deficit through any means. Some level of stress is an additional factor that could increase your risk further. The stress component can be as simple as a perceived pressure to lose weight.

- Fear of weight gain is a convenient narrative that we have created in our modern Western culture to explain restrictive eating disorders. Restrictive eating disorders are not, at their core, a fear of weight gain. People through history and those today from non-Western cultures with restrictive eating disorders, such as anorexia, did not and do not attribute their symptoms to a fear of weight gain. That's not to say that people today don't have a very strong aversion to the idea of gaining weight or being in a bigger body. Many do. However, restrictive eating disorders are a powerful addiction to energy deficit with a once-beneficial evolutionary purpose.

- Anyone who is in a semi-starved state will experience extreme hunger (also called hyperphagia). This can drive you to eat in excess of 10,000 calories a day when your brain perceives that food is available. This is not binge eating disorder. It is a normal physiological response to hunger and starvation. The high hunger settles down when your body is fully out of energy deficit and has restored both fat and lean tissues (allowing for overshoot).

- You CAN overcome a restrictive eating disorder. No matter how long you have had an eating disorder or how entrenched you believe it to be, it is possible. It will be incredibly hard and you will need support. You need to allow for full brain reprogramming and to go through very challenging emotions. You also need to let your body fully restore so that you completely emerge from energy deficit. Aiming for overshoot provides you with your best chance of success with this!

The above synopsis of *Addicted to Energy Deficit* is a very condensed version. A lot more information is covered in the first book than can be summarised. However, a basic understanding of these key points will help you as you read through the information in this handbook so that you can get as much value from it as possible.

Helly x

GLOSSARY OF TERMS

Amygdala The region of the brain primarily involved in emotional processing. It's commonly thought of as the part of the brain that drives a fight or flight fear response.

Chewing and spitting A habitual behaviour seen in people with restrictive eating disorders in which they chew food but rather than consume it will spit it out.

Craving An overwhelming urge to engage in a behaviour or use a substance. Feelings of irritability, anxiety or fear are common with cravings.

Dopamine A form of neurotransmitter which when released in the brain has a rewarding effect and is a key chemical in motivation and goal pursuit. Dopamine plays a critical role in addiction. Having the right levels of dopamine is important for the brain and body.

Endogenous (or natural) opioids A more general term for enkephalins and endorphins. These naturally produced hormones act in the same way as morphine and other opioid substances and can create feelings of euphoria, stimulating the brain's reward system.

Endorphins and enkephalins Naturally occurring hormones that are released by the brain and send messages through the body. They can relieve pain, reduce stress and improve mood and in this way are thought of as *feel-good* chemicals. These are more specific terms for natural opioids.

Energy deficit A physiological state in which the body has insufficient energy in relation to energy coming in and/or stored energy supplies to meet its requirements.

Hyperphagia or extreme hunger A physiological drive to eat extremely high amounts of food as a natural biological response to semi-starvation. Extreme hunger occurs when the body is in a state of energy deficit with insufficient fat and lean tissue stores in relation to the genetically determined level it requires. This is not the same as binge eating because with extreme hunger, people maintain a sense of control in whether or not they respond to it, whereas binge eating is defined by a sense of loss of control over eating a lot of food in a short space of time.

Metabolism All the chemical processes that occur in the body or an organism to sustain life. These processes require energy so metabolism is directly linked to energy availability and use.

Neural networks and circuits Brain pathways made up of connecting neurons form into complete networks and circuits that drive particular habits, behaviours, thought patterns and beliefs. Any new learning is wired into the brain to form into neural circuits for that particular learning. Networks develop when the circuits for different behavioural and thought pattens intertwine, whereby one action will precede or coincide with the other, so the circuits driving each become interlinked.

Neuron A basic cell of the nervous system that sends and receives electro-chemical signals to other cells. The brain is made up of billions of neurons which connect to and communicate with one another to form circuits and networks driving habits, thoughts, emotions and behaviours.

Neuroplasticity The brain's ability to reshape and change throughout the lifespan in response to new learning and circumstances, allowing the development of new habits and ability to *unlearn* old ones. This is commonly referred to as *rewiring*.

Neurotransmitter A chemical that is released by one neuron to communicate with the next. In addiction, dopamine is a key neurotransmitter.

Overshoot or fat overshoot A body fully recovering from a state of semi-starvation needs to gain excess fat supplies in order to be able to restore and repair all lean tissue stores and fully emerge from energy deficit. Once this has been achieved, the overshoot fat will naturally subside, without conscious effort to lose it.

Pre Frontal Cortex (PFC) A section of the brain located at the front of the frontal lobe (just behind the forehead). The PFC is the intellectual centre of the brain, responsible for regulating behaviours through planning, decision making and impulse control.

Quasi-Recovery A term widely used in eating disorder communities to describe someone with an eating disorder who has made some progress to overcome it but remains very driven by compulsive habits and behaviours related to the pursuit of energy deficit, leaving them living a *half-life*.

Rituals A particular way of behaving or thinking that has high importance placed on it, with an associated drive to repeat it in the same way time and again. Rituals become habitual and so are often performed with little conscious awareness. In themselves, rituals can become part of wider addictive patterns and often serve as cues to full engagement in an addictive behaviour or drug.

Set point theory The understanding that every body has a largely genetically determined set point level for weight that it will fight to maintain. It is now understood that this relates to set point levels for fat and lean tissue stores that the brain recognises as minimally necessary for that individual to be in energy balance.

Synapse A space between two neurons across which the two cells communicate with one another by the release and uptake of chemicals (also called neurotransmitters). Synapses are the connection between neurons that allow them to communicate and form wider pathways, circuits and networks.

Introduction

Aiming for Overshoot is a practical guide which I hope you will find informative, inspirational and reassuring. But most of all, I hope it helps you to feel less alone in a process that can be incredibly lonely when so few people understand what you are up against.

Overcoming a restrictive eating disorder is probably the hardest thing you will do in your lifetime but I believe that everyone has the potential to do it, no matter how long you have had an eating disorder or how deeply entrenched it has become.

The content of this book is written for people with restrictive eating disorders of all ages, genders, races, religions, sexualities and most importantly of all, it's for people of all body types.

It's an indisputable fact that all forms of restrictive eating disorders, including anorexia nervosa, occur in people of all body sizes. In fact, anorexia is now known to be more common in people in a *normal* or *above* BMI range than people below *normal* weight by BMI[1]. And the symptoms, severity, risks and consequences are just the same or greater[2]. Therefore, your body size and weight are irrelevant. If you have a restrictive eating disorder, which means you have an addiction to the state of energy deficit and are suppressing your natural body weight, this book is for you.

This book is also for anyone who has *attempted recovery* and gained some weight but still hasn't been able to overcome all the powerful compulsive behaviours and restrictive eating. The weight you have gained is largely irrelevant to the fact that you still have significant brain reprogramming work to do and that in all likelihood you do need to accept and tolerate further weight gain to fully emerge from energy deficit.

All this is to say that I hope you feel included and understand that the content of this book is for you, no matter who you are or what your situation is.

The coming chapters contain a mixture of my personal experiences as I went through the messy process to overcome an eating disorder and the training, knowledge and skills that I've gained through my current professional work as a coach for others overcoming eating disorders. Parts of the book incorporate blog posts and journal entries I wrote when I was going through the process. Where appropriate, there is neuroscience and research to back up the information and advice given. Whether the chapters are factual, anecdotal or humorous, I aim to keep the book real and sensitive.

Aiming for Overshoot is a book you can dip in and out of when you need information and inspiration or as a way to give yourself a pep talk,

> *It's a bad day and I'm not sure that I can push on but I'm going to find my way through.*

Take from the book what you need and leave what you don't.

1. Harrop EN, Mensinger JL, Moore M, Lindhorst T. Restrictive eating disorders in higher weight persons: A systematic review of atypical anorexia
   nervosa prevalence and consecutive admission literature. Int J Eat Disord.
   2021 Aug;54(8):1328-1357. doi: 10.1002/eat.23519. Epub 2021 Apr 17.
   PMID: 33864277; PMCID: PMC9035356.

2. Golden NH, Mehler PS. Atypical anorexia nervosa can be just as bad.
   Cleve Clin J Med. 2020 Mar;87(3):172-174. doi: 10.3949/ccjm.87a.191
   46. PMID: 32127441.

Chapter 1

Why Aim for Overshoot?

Y ou are likely reading this now with an inner dialogue very similar to the following:

Why did I pick up a book with a title that strikes fear into my heart? What possessed me? Aiming for overshoot is not only terrifying but the idea is also insane.

Why would I aim for overshoot? I hate how just gaining a couple of pounds makes me feel.

I hear your concerns. But take a few deep breaths and read on with an open mind and a hopeful heart.

Firstly, correct me if I'm wrong, but the reason you have picked up and chosen to read a book called, *Aiming for Overshoot*, is that a restrictive eating disorder is making your life miserable. Eating disorders are destructive. They impact every aspect of how you live and your ability to live authentically. It's likely you are often anxious and unhappy or numb and the only way to block this reality is by engaging in the eating disorder behaviours causing it. You are hungry, driven and unable to relax and you know that life should be much easier than it is. And perhaps, a gut feeling tells you that this idea of deliberately pursuing overshoot could hold credibility.

To help you understand the credibility behind the idea of pursuing overshoot to overcome a restrictive eating disorder let's go back to some neurobiology.

Perhaps one of the main reasons that overshoot is something you should not only stop avoiding but actually aim for is that overshoot is needed to get you out of the current state of energy deficit that your brain is addicted to. *Addicted to Energy Deficit* explains why your body goes through a process of fat over-shoot when it's restoring from a semi-starved state and that this fat overshoot is necessary to ensure your body can fully restore and repair all lean tissues. Only when your body has fully gained both fat and lean tissue stores will your brain recognise that you are in energy balance. Once back in energy balance, you finally reach a physical state that will allow you to also fully overcome the eating disorder on a brain-based level. Without fat overshoot, you don't escape energy deficit and so won't overcome the eating disorder.

The next important point is that to overcome a restrictive eating disorder, you don't just need to restore your body but brain reprogramming is also critical. The brain networks that have become deeply embedded over the years of your addiction to the pursuit of energy deficit need to be unwired and your brain needs to wire in new circuits that will drive behaviours of unrestricted eating without compulsions to compensate. A detailed neuroscience-based explanation for why the best method to fully reprogram your brain is by full abstinence from restrictive eating and all the eating disorder behaviours is in *Addicted to Energy Deficit*.

But, how do you abstain from these things? You stop behaving like someone aiming to lose or closely control their weight and start acting like someone who wants to gain weight. If you are actively aiming to gain weight then you will do all the things that are most beneficial to your brain rewiring process. For example, you will eat frequently and abundantly with foods that are dense and high in calories and fats while not doing anything that will unnecessarily expend energy because you can't afford to waste it. If you are deliberately aiming for overshoot, you essentially take on the necessary abstinence mindset that will get you where you need to be—towards a brain that is reprogramming very effectively as your body restores and fully emerges from energy deficit. In this way, you address both sides of the process together, with quicker and more effective results.

Staying with some neuroscience for a moment longer—when you are fully focused and determined on overshoot, your brain will also recognise this deliberate pursuit and pay more attention to what you are focused on doing. This will ensure your brain notices that these behaviours pursuing weight gain are intentional. It will recognise them as a good thing, making it more likely that your deep learning (or *rewiring)* process is faster and that the new brain circuits being built become stronger and deeper.

Aside from these science-based explanations, why else would you aim for overshoot?

Perhaps you were intrigued by the title of this book because you have been through eating disorder treatment or attempted to overcome the eating disorder yourself and haven't yet reached the freedom you know is out there. You know there has to be a way to overcome this eating disorder but the approaches you have tried haven't felt quite right or ever taken you far enough so you stayed stuck or slid backwards. The old saying that, *If you always do what you have always done, you will always get what you always got,* is true. Why would the outcome be different if you keep pursuing *recovery* in ways you have before? It's time to try an approach that might seem extreme or terrifying but perhaps it might also actually work.

Finally, I suspect that you have picked up a book that's encouraging the pursuit of weight gain to the point of overshoot because, as uncomfortable as you are with this level of weight gain, at a deeper level, you want to move past the aversion to gaining weight. You want to eat all the food you are hungry for and to rest your weary body and mind in ways that might make you gain weight but that will also come with intense relief because you no longer have to spend every day hungry, cold and driven.

The people who do overcome restrictive eating disorders empower themselves. They develop tools and find support to break eating disorder habits and restrictive eating patterns in bolder ways than those who don't. They let the weight gain happen, accepting overshoot, without attempting to manipulate it, even if at first they struggle with their changing body. They hold on and push through. They learn that life is so much better in a body that's no longer in energy deficit and when their minds are free to live with more authenticity than was ever possible with the eating disorder. You can have this too. Become empowered and aim for overshoot!

Chapter 2

Suppress Your Body = Suppress Your Life

N ow you understand why to aim for overshoot, it's also worth considering the impact of suppressing your natural body weight.

With a restrictive eating disorder and a brain-based addiction to energy deficit, a lot of your focus and time is spent on thoughts and behaviours related to the suppression of your natural body weight, shape and size.

Let's explore that further.

When you consider the word, *suppress,* it comes from Latin and translates to be, *pressed down.* When you are actively suppressing your true weight and shape every day, you are pressing down on your body and its natural ability to function in all the ways it could and should. Other definitions of *suppress*, relate to the prevention of being seen and expressed, or something forcibly ended[1].

While you continue to live a life every day in which you are suppressing your natural body weight and size through behaviours that are compulsive and addictive, you are being constantly pressed down, prevented from true expression and being seen. If you continue in this way, it could also tragically but not unrealistically, lead to a *forcible end* because restrictive eating disorders can be that serious.

Our body, mind and essence of being are all connected and so when you suppress one, you suppress the others. When you are suppressing your natural body weight and size, not allowing it to be seen and expressed in the way it needs to thrive, you also suppress your ability to thrive in so many other ways.

How can your mind and spirit thrive when your body is being suppressed? They can't and they won't. While you are living in a body that's incapable of being all it needs to be, your mind will also be constricted and prevented from true expression and your spirit, sense of self and authenticity can't be seen. Suppressing your natural body weight is suppressing all that you are and all that you could be. I don't doubt that what I'm saying holds very true to your reality with the eating disorder.

Happily, there is an alternative.

You can move forward into an unsuppressed life. Stop suppressing your natural body weight and embrace all that your body needs to be—the size, shape and weight. This will enable you to live an unsuppressed life so that you are no longer pressing down on your mind and soul. You can then let yourself live authentically and allow yourself to be seen. The importance of authenticity as you are overcoming an eating disorder is explored in more depth in Chapter 4.

Decide that you will no longer suppress your natural body weight and instead let it be the size and shape that nature intended. Achieve this by aiming for overshoot. In this way, you will find a life in which the person you should always have been can emerge to express themselves and be seen in every fabulous way!

---

1. https://dictionary.cambridge.org/dictionary/english/suppress

Chapter 3

Self-Empowerment Underlies Everything

M y intention with this book was to leave very few questions unanswered concerning how you abstain from the eating disorder, reprogram your brain, restore your body and rebuild your life.

But, the trait you need more than any other in this process is self-empowerment. Ensure that you are taking control and feeling empowered on your journey. The impact of the changes you make will not be as significant if you are not in the driving seat compared to when you decisively take charge and develop belief in your ability to do so.

The importance of self-empowerment is covered in depth in *Addicted to Energy Deficit*. But because this is such an important component of the process, it's worth reiterating some aspects of why self-empowerment matters and how you can develop it. After all, for some of you, self-empowerment, particularly with the eating disorder, might have been lacking for a long time.

Own Your Recovery

Here I am, telling you that self-empowerment is something you need to develop and that you will find overcoming the eating disorder much harder without it, but I haven't defined it. Self-empowerment is a term that sounds great and idealistic but what does it mean and importantly, what's involved?

Well, a quick Google* of *self-empowerment* will tell you from any number of websites, blogs and experts, that self-empowerment means to, *take charge of your life,* or some even say of your *destiny* (very grand!). The consensus seems to be that when you are self-empowered, you take control of your life and make decisions that are in your best interest, setting goals, learning, growing and developing confidence, while building your community and using support as you do so.

Or, as I like to put it, it means *owning your recovery!*

You need to be in control when you are overcoming an eating disorder so your brain understands that the difficult changes you are making are important. When it perceives these changes as important, it's more likely to unwire the deeply entrenched eating disorder networks and build new circuits that drive the habits you are developing, taking you away from an eating-disordered life. To form any new habits, it's necessary to be in control of that learning and direct your brain in the direction you want it to go. This way it understands why this new and difficult learning is important to you. If someone else is in charge of the changes you are making and you are doing them because you are *told to* rather than because you are motivated and driven to do so, your brain is not going to be particularly interested in building those changes into meaningful new pathways. Therefore, when the pressure to make the changes is gone, very little will have changed in your brain's wiring.

This is why you need to take control. Get in the driver's seat and own your recovery. Build on your *why* for doing this and feel rubbish but do it anyway. When you do, your confidence and self-belief will naturally grow that this is something you CAN do.

Some additional tips are provided below for how to develop self-empowerment as you go through the process to overcome the eating disorder, aiming for overshoot. A few of these are covered in more detail in later chapters.

Tips to Build Self-Empowerment

- Reclaim your control from the eating disorder. Develop confidence that you can.

- Stop seeking permission from others.

- Give yourself permission to succeed—permission to overcome the eating disorder, to eat, rest and gain weight.

- Develop a Feck It attitude—*I'm doing this MY way and I'll enjoy the process!*

- Decide the steps to take that you believe will work for you and make them happen.

- Avoid blaming others when things don't go as planned.

- Don't wait to be told what to do or for someone else to notice that you haven't had lunch yet. Take responsibility.

- Build a support team made up of professionals, family, friends, a coach, the cat(!) and anyone else. Stay in the pilot's seat and allow your team members to be your wingmen, helping you move forward.

- Use lapses as learning opportunities.

- Be reflective and reflect on your progress regularly. What's working? What isn't? What needs to change? How can this be achieved?

- Set regular goals and intentions and find ways to be accountable for them.

- Move away from the eating disorder identity. Begin to identify as someone *overcoming* an eating disorder and who *had* an eating disorder.

- Build a future vision of what your life can look like without an eating disorder in it. What do you want from that future? Imagine your future-self pulling you towards them in magical ways.

- If you can't picture a free future yet or the thought of doing so creates anxiety, just hold onto the hope that one day at a time, your future will evolve into something better than it is now.

- Don't believe anyone who has told you that you can't beat this. Have faith in all you can achieve. Your brain can reprogram, your body can heal and you can overcome this eating disorder.

- Develop your self-trust. Remind yourself that just because you haven't succeeded before doesn't mean you can't or won't.

- Choose to overcome the eating disorder every single day. Choose more food. Choose not to engage in compensatory behaviours. Choose to tolerate difficult emotions and anxiety. Choose to gain weight. Choose to find your freedom.

- Allow yourself to recognise that you are winning—be proud, build your confidence and develop your self worth.

- Believe in your power and ability to do this and do it!

other search engines are available!

Chapter 4

Becoming Authentic & Vulnerable

I n content related to overcoming restrictive eating disorders, there's often a strong focus on food, compensatory behaviours and a lot of conversation about weight gain. Of course, it's critical to address all these things. You don't get far without eating a lot more food to overcome restriction, abstaining from compulsive compensatory behaviours or emerging from energy deficit, involving inevitable weight gain. But there's rarely sufficient focus on some of the less practical aspects of the process to find freedom from an eating disorder. Yet without these, success might remain out of reach. This chapter covers two of these critical factors—learning to become more authentically you and in so doing, allowing yourself to be vulnerable.

Now, before you roll your eyes at me and start searching for the bit of the book where you are told to eat more food, please grab a couple of Mars bars and hear me out because this is also important.

What Does Being Authentic Mean?

Authenticity means to be in touch with yourself, your body, feelings and emotions. It's being able to connect to your gut feelings and respond to them. Our gut feelings are some of the most trusted and deeply connected senses that we have, stemming from evolution. Our ancestors survived because they relied on their gut feelings and instincts.

The gut is now considered to be your *second brain*. It's made up of around 100 million neurons (nerve cells) which produce over thirty different neurochemicals more typically associated with the brain. The vagus nerve runs between your brain and your gut, sending messages between these two organs at very high speeds. Ninety percent of these signals are sent from your gut to your brain, impacting your thoughts and perceptions[1].

Trusting your gut instincts allows you to connect more authentically to yourself, what you are feeling and your desires. Intuition and gut feelings are made up of a huge amount of processing that your brain has undertaken from sensory information coming in, current experiences and memories, to predict what will happen next and formulate decisions about how to act. This all happens unconsciously and results in you getting a gut feeling to take a certain course of action[2]. It's when you continuously suppress your gut instincts that you lose the ability to live authentically and go against key processes that were created for you to thrive.

You are also likely to have lost touch with your authenticity if you felt the need to blunt it to fit in with others, such as your society, culture or family. If being yourself comes with a threat of being rejected and losing connection to others, it makes you more afraid to be yourself. As a connection to others is also an evolutionary survival need, it can lead you to prioritise that connection at the cost of your authenticity.

But what happens when you live a life not being authentic and feeling unable to show the world who you are?

If you don't feel safe enough to show people your true self, then no one can really know you and any relationships you have will remain unfulfilling. This will leave you feeling alone, even when you are with loved ones or in a group. You are likely to suppress strong emotions and your desires with what you want to do, who you want to become and how you want to live, to fit in or please others. This results in internal frustration and inner conflict or pain. But it will manifest in a way that you hide from others, so that you continue to block your gut instincts, emotions and any justified anger.

With an eating disorder, you are very likely to have lost any ability you once had to live a more authentic life. It's possible that over the years, you have hidden and blunted your true self and that attempts to fit into a diet culture-influenced society made you scared to show the world who you are. When the eating disorder took hold, it will have also crushed any ability you had to connect more deeply to your inner values and instincts.

An eating disorder, like any addiction, is a powerful tool to numb emotions and block pain and it becomes a key coping mechanism for life stress. However, when you live in an addicted and driven way, where your main focus each day is on how to continue to chase the *drug* your brain craves (energy deficit), you lose the ability to experience real emotions or connect to yourself. This is one more reason why the eating disorder has thrived in the way it has and remains so hard to overcome.

Authenticity is also killed when you take care of the needs of others and neglect your own. All too often, constantly saying yes to other people and their demands on you means that you say no to yourself and the things you need, so you suffer all the more. This is something people with eating disorders can excel at. To overcome the eating disorder, you need to learn to stop saying yes to others and their demands on you when doing so means you are saying no to your ability to make the necessary changes to overcome the eating disorder. When you have overcome the eating disorder and started to live with authenticity, the people around you will get more from you than they ever can now.

When you continue to live an inauthentic life, you remain afraid to show the world who you are in a physical, emotional and spiritual sense. This means you can't move forwards, you will struggle to let the needed weight gain happen and you will continue to rely on the eating disorder to numb your real emotions. To let the eating disorder go, you need to find ways to reconnect to your authentic self. For this, you will need to learn who that person is and then let others see you too. This means being vulnerable enough to allow others to know you and it entails facing difficult emotions and processing pain and anger. It's hard but you are unlikely to find a meaningful or fulfilling life beyond the eating disorder if you don't.

If you continue to block your authenticity but you do manage to overcome the eating disorder, it will likely come at the cost of switching to another form of addictive disorder or less healthy coping methods that keep you numbed and block your reality.

Being Vulnerable

There's no denying that although showing up to the world with authenticity can bring huge rewards and means you can live your life feeling connected and fulfilled, it does also necessitate being vulnerable. It means letting people know the real you and that comes with a risk of rejection or hurt:

Vulnerability is our susceptibility to be wounded. It is part of our
fragility and cannot be escaped[3]

However, you can choose to be vulnerable, connecting to yourself and others in more meaningful ways. Unless you open the door to vulnerability and to showing up authentically with others, not only will your connection to your instincts and self be blunted but so too will any real connection to the people in your life. This will mean that any relationships will remain at a surface level because no one can really know you.

When you speak to people who have overcome eating disorders, other addictions or significant illnesses, many will tell you that, in part, they are grateful the disorder or illness happened to them because it enabled them to find their true selves and live authentically in a way they never would have otherwise.

Learn to trust your gut instincts and intuition, begin to get in touch your true self, allow yourself to be vulnerable and show the world who you are in a life you feel connected to. It might be that is a life that takes a different trajectory from the one you imagined you would be on but that's ok. Find fulfilment and freedom by not just eating and overcoming all the addictive behaviours but adding into your process the key factors of authenticity and vulnerability.

How Do You Start to Live More Authentically?

Just like everything in life that's important, your ability to live authentically is an evolving process but it's also one that you can apply more focus to today. It will take courage, self-awareness and reflection and it won't always be easy but it will be worth it.

1. Begin by tuning in to what the true you wants concerning food and

rest, recognising the deeply buried cries of hunger and urges to eat the things you have denied yourself for so long. Listen to the voice saying, *Please let me curl up and rest today.* Recognise that these very blunted whispers for more food and rest are coming from your authentic self and from a body that's crying out for these things to reach a place of energy balance and health. Respond to these messages, moving away from your habitual ways to keep busy or please others that usually act as a means to suppress your genuine needs.

2. Practise not always saying yes to others when it means you are saying no to your needs and your ability to overcome the eating disorder. Prioritise your health and your ability to live with authenticity. People will respect you more for it in the long run.

3. When you do feel upset, hurt, angry or irritable then acknowledge it first to yourself and then talk to someone you trust and begin to be vulnerable with others too. An astute observation by Gabor Mate is, *Nothing in nature grows without being vulnerable.* Be vulnerable so that you can grow.

4. If you have pain from the past concerning things that have happened to you or things that you have done, acknowledge that the pain is there and that it hurts. Don't try to block, deny or invalidate it. Then remind yourself that you can't change the things that have happened in the past but you can choose how to move forward and to live by your values today. If you are struggling with past trauma or emotions that you can't move beyond then consider using therapy to help you with this.

5. Learn to tune into your gut instincts and intuition when they strike. When you get an inner sense that something feels wrong, whether it's with a decision, action or relationship then listen to it, even if you can't make sense of it. Gut instincts come from your authentic self and are important, so explore them.

6. Journal or self-reflect each day. Explore what you did today that was true to your values and allowed you to be authentic. Reflect on how to build on these things. Then reflect on where in the day you blunted your true instincts, needs or desires and ignored your authenticity. When you do this, you can explore ways to move forward while avoiding old patterns.

7. Remember who you were in the past, before the eating disorder or at another time when you did live a more authentic life (if such a time exists). Acknowledge who you were then and what parts of that person are still within you, seeking ways to re-emerge.

8. In *Addicted to Energy Deficit*, the importance of self-identity for your ability to overcome the eating disorder is explained. Let the eating disorder identity go and create an identity related to who you are as a stronger person who has had an eating disorder but for whom that history is only one part of their wider identity today. This is also crucial to be able to live with authenticity. When you let the eating disorder identity go, allow the space to be there in which you have lost the old identity but not yet developed a new sense of who you are. It's not a comfortable space to be in but it's an important one, giving you time to connect to what you do want, your feelings and emotions and the things that make life meaningful for you.

9. Recognise that learning to live authentically and with greater vulnerability takes practice. It's another key component to the necessary brain rewiring as you reprogram your brain away from the eating disorder networks.

10. Don't be afraid to make life changes. When you begin to live with more authenticity and emerge from the depths of an eating disorder after what might be years or decades, you might realise that the life you built when you weren't able to be authentic isn't the life you want now. Explore changes you know will enable you to live a life you feel

more connected to and fulfilled by and do it. You won't regret it.

---

1. https://neuroscience.ubc.ca/our-second-brain-more-than-a-gut-feeling/

2. https://neurosciencenews.com/gut-feelings-9082/

3. Maté, Gabor. In the Realm of Hungry Ghosts: Close Encounters with Addiction. London, UK: Vermilion, 2018. Chicago, 17th ed.

Chapter 5

Commitment

You might have asked yourself the following question or had it asked of you by others when yet again you have given in to another powerful eating disordered compulsion:

Are you committed to overcoming the eating disorder or not?

Commitment is a word that gets used a lot with overcoming eating disorders. And doesn't it sound great to be able to say,

I'm fully committed to overcoming this eating disorder!

On the surface, to be committed to the process and your free future sounds wonderful. But what does it really mean?

What Does Commitment Mean?

One motivational quote defines commitment as,

Doing the thing you said you would do, long after the mood in which you said it has left you.

When you committed to overcoming the eating disorder, your levels of optimism, hope, positivity, excitement and passion at doing so were possibly already wavering. Even at the start, your commitment is likely to have come with a sprinkling of trepidation and underlying anxiety.

But if you have committed, it means you do whatever it takes to see your commitment through, no matter how you feel about continuing or how much anxiety and distress it creates.

Commitment Involves Acting on Your Intentions

When you commit you are not saying *try* or *maybe*. You are saying *I will* and *I am* and *I'm doing it!*

When the actions you take to reach your goals aren't working, then being committed means that you don't just give up but you establish what needs to change and the support you need to ensure that your commitment is actively realised.

If slips or lapses occur, being committed means that you recognise what's happened, identify what triggered it, put in place measures to prevent the same from happening again and move on with greater determination.

But a commitment to overcoming an eating disorder, like any commitment, needs to be 100% even if it's frightening to make that pledge. Allow in any room for doubt or hesitation and when your brain is in hot pursuit of the dopamine hit it craves from energy deficit, your defences will be too low to stop it.

To say you are committed but leave room for doubt will result in a greater risk of excuses and procrastination. When doubt creeps in, the potential for *get out* increases at an alarming rate and soon your best-laid intentions fall by the wayside.

Signs Of Not Being Fully Committed

- Delaying action. Always saying *tomorrow* or after x event.

- All talk, no action.

- Repeating methods that haven't worked before, staying in the same cycles, which feel safe but also keep you stuck.

- Being trapped in the one step forwards, two-back game, rather than continuing even when it gets tough.

- Confusion about what you are doing or why.

- Constant doubt, which creates overwhelming anxiety.

- Allowing a wobble in your intentions to be an excuse to give up.

To be committed means doing what you set out to with intent and action, no matter what. It means diligence, integrity and clear goals.

When you are committed to the process to overcoming the eating disorder, you allow yourself to begin to connect to your authentic self and become true to who you are beyond it. When you begin to get a sense of the real you returning, the doubts that you are committed to the right goals will almost certainly go, leaving you experiencing a greater sense of inner calm and peace.

Committing to overcoming the eating disorder fully and finally is hard. But say it out loud,

I am committed to do whatever it takes to be free of this eating disorder!

Repeat it each and every day, several times a day if you have to. Keep that promise to yourself and rather than just talk the talk, do it.

Chapter 6

The Additional Challenges of Being in a Bigger Body

I've tried to be clear throughout this book and *Addicted to Energy Deficit*, that the information applies equally to anyone with a restrictive eating disorder, irrespective of your body size, weight or shape. It's finally becoming (*slightly*) more widely recognised that restrictive eating disorders don't have a size. Slowly, eating disorder *professionals* are being forced to acknowledge that someone can be just as mentally and physically compromised with a restrictive eating disorder in a plus-size body as someone with a very low body mass index.

The psychiatric diagnostic bible, also called the DSM-5[1] has now introduced a separate category for a form of anorexia nervosa (AN) called *atypical anorexia*. For this diagnosis, you need to meet all the same diagnostic criteria as for AN but your, *weight remains within or above the normal weight range, despite significant weight loss*. It's a step forward that the DSM now recognises that people can have anorexia in bodies that are not emaciated. In an ideal world, it wouldn't be a separate entry to the existing AN category and instead an AN diagnosis would be inclusive of all current body sizes. Perhaps though, the most misleading and unhelpful aspect of this recent DSM entry is the use of the term *atypical*. The reality is that *atypical* anorexia is one of the most common eating disorders. By current diagnostic criteria, *atypical* anorexia is far more typical than non-atypical anorexia. In fact, it's currently believed to be around three times more common[2] and while people with atypical anorexia remain less likely to receive an accurate diagnosis due to existing stereotypes, the true figure is likely to be higher still.

Studies are also increasingly demonstrating that restrictive eating disorders in people in the *healthy, overweight* or *obese* ranges face the same cardiovascular and other health risks as someone at the lower BMI spectrum. These risks include a low heart rate and other heart arrhythmias, electrolyte imbalances and bone density loss. Females with anorexia in larger bodies are just as likely to experience a loss of their menstrual cycle and hormonal changes. Any weight suppression of just 5% below your genetic set weight range is of significance in terms of the medical complications it can create[345].

For people at higher weights, the psychological symptoms can also be more significant than in those at lower weights, with greater preoccupation around food avoidance and negative feelings about body shape and weight.

Despite all the evidence that current body shape and size don't equate to how affected someone is by an eating disorder, it will come as no surprise to you that people at higher weights are under-diagnosed and have symptoms for longer, with a higher level of weight loss before they are diagnosed. And once diagnosed, they are less likely to be offered intensive treatment[6].

The take-home message is that things are changing although all too slowly. However, if you have a restrictive eating disorder in a higher-weight body then please know that you are no *less sick*, less at risk or deserving of support and treatment than anyone else. The eating disorder affecting you is valid and just as critical.

The next question is what advice should you follow if you are in a bigger body and have an active restrictive eating disorder?

When it comes to the information and guidance in both this book and *Addicted to Energy Deficit,* it all applies equally to anyone with a restrictive eating disorder, no matter your body shape or weight. The advice to abstain from restriction and all your addictive compensatory behaviours, habits and rituals is the same, as is the advice to do everything possible to emerge from your current energy deficit state and aim for overshoot.

I recognise though that it can feel impossible to find the motivation and courage to gain weight when you are in a body that's already considered *healthy* or in the *overweight* or *obese* range. Not only are you up against a restrictive eating disorder, with its addictive drive to keep you in energy deficit and at a suppressed weight, but to then deliberately gain weight in a culture that frowns upon weight gain and focuses too much on the dangers of obesity and obesity *epidemics* is an extra hurdle that I wish you didn't have to face. Unfortunately, to find mental and physical freedom, it's an extra hurdle you will need to jump.

Those of you who know my history might consider this to be a topic that I shouldn't write about. I admit that this wasn't an issue I had to navigate and I don't know first-hand what you are facing. However, I have worked as a coach with clients who are overcoming restrictive eating disorders from a starting point of being in a body that is within the normal or above range and so I have their additional experience to pull on as well as years' worth of knowledge and experience in this field.

At the end of the day, this topic is extremely important and the more people writing or speaking about it is surely a good thing.

How to Aim for Overshoot from a *Normal* or Plus-Sized Body

- Firstly, scream, shout, cry and get mad that the world is as it is and that it's unfair that diet culture makes this so much harder for you than it should be because it is unfair. Feel it and let it out. Don't suppress these valid emotions. Then take some deep breaths and focus on moving forwards.

- Learn all you can about set weight theories, the importance of fat overshoot and the clear evidence that demonstrates that any weight-suppressed body is not optimally healthy. This information will help you to rationalise the need to abstain from restriction and other weight-suppressing behaviours when the eating disorder thoughts and urges are stronger. There is a lot of information about the science of set point theory and fat overshoot in *Addicted to Energy Deficit*. You might also explore some of the excellent materials available on the dangers of the diet industry and diet culture, to surround yourself with information that will support the steps you need to take.

- If your body didn't need to gain weight, then resting and eating what you need by listening and responding to your body wouldn't lead to weight gain. The weight gained as you abstain from the eating disorder is therefore necessary for your body and healthy for you.

- The mantra that overcoming an eating disorder is about, *mental state and not weight* is excellent because it's true. Weight gain is a side effect of the very necessary work needed to fix an addicted mental state, which you can achieve by using the approach advocated throughout this book. Your mental state won't change without weight gain but the focus should be on ensuring that your mental state is changing because that's where your full freedom lies.

- You won't believe it until it happens but most people find that once they have gained the necessary weight to overcome the eating disorder, their whole life is so much wider, more positive and hopeful, that the weight is something they accept more easily than they ever believed possible. This is as true for those who gain into plus-size bodies as for those who gain weight but remain in a smaller one.

- Reflect on what you love and value in others. It's unlikely to be their body shape or size.

- Focus on your inner values and what matters to you in life—your true values beyond body shape and weight.

- Remind yourself that overcoming the eating disorder will mean you can break free from the narrow, focused, driven and rigid world that the eating disorder creates. This will give you the ability to love, laugh and experience joy again in ways that are impossible when imprisoned by an eating disorder's addictive drive.

- Picture what you want from your future, irrespective of your body size. Envision it in all its technicoloured magical details, striving towards it with more food.

- When you picture that bigger and more colourful life, allow yourself to feel excited about your body, the foods you can eat and where it will all take you as both your internal and external worlds open up.

- Follow body positive people—those who are proud in their skin at plus-sizes and who don't let a bigger body hold them back from their aspirations. Decide to be as proud of your own growing body and as determined that you can achieve anything you want because of it, not in spite of it.

- Know that overcoming this eating disorder and gaining weight into a body bigger than you feel comfortable with will make you a very powerful, strong and insightful person.

- Be authentic to yourself and learn to be vulnerable with others. This is something that takes courage but when you do, it allows you to live without suppressing either your natural weight and shape or your true personality and authenticity.

- Think about what your body does for you and can give you, not what size it is and be appreciative of it.

- Dress your body in clothes that make you feel great and colours and fabrics that you love.

- You don't have to hide your body just because it's bigger. If you want to proudly show off your curves in tight-fitting clothes then don't let anyone tell you that you can't!

- Consider your social circles. If the people you spend time with are all in smaller bodies and pursuing weight loss behaviours then it will make it harder for you. Seek out social groups who are happy in their skin at any size and begin to notice the diverse range of body shapes and sizes that are living happily and healthily in this world.

- When you are looking to social media for inspiration from others, decide instead to be the inspiration you seek.

- If memories from the past of being bullied, teased or told to lose weight are impacting you, then remember that that was then and people who judge you for your weight aren't worthy of your time. There are plenty of people in the world who will love and respect you for being who you are, at the size you become and the size you should always have been.

- Educate others. I agree that you shouldn't have to but the more that you do, the easier it could become for you. Educate the people who matter—your loved ones and your doctor and your health care team about why you need to gain weight from this starting point and have to let your body find its natural set weight. Give them information to read if that helps and ask them not to give you weight loss or healthy living advice.

It sucks that people have to go through the process of overcoming a restrictive eating disorder, deliberately pursuing weight gain in a culture that frowns upon bigger bodies. But it's the culture that's wrong and gaining weight as you overcome the eating disorder is the right thing to do for the sake of your future life and ability to live it freely. You can and will deal with the weight gain better than you think you will but of course it won't be easy. Even though every fibre of your core might be screaming at you that you don't want to gain weight, choose to aim for overshoot and embrace it, pushing yourself to adopt a positive and excited attitude as you discover the freedoms you crave. The more you determinedly choose your future instead of the eating disorder's pursuit of energy deficit, the sooner you will become the person who is happy and proud in their bigger body, no matter what size it is.

---

1. American Psychiatric Association. Diagnostic and statistical manual of mental disorders. 2022 (5th ed., text rev.). https://doi.org/10.1176/appi.books.9780890425787.

2. Stice E, Marti CN, Rohde P. Prevalence, incidence, impairment, and course of the proposed DSM-5 eating disorder diagnoses in an 8-year prospective community study of young women. J Abnorm Psychol. 2013 May;122(2):445-57. doi: 10.1037/a0030679. Epub 2012 Nov 12. PMID: 23148784; PMCID: PMC3980846.

3. University of California - San Francisco. Anorexia nervosa comes in all sizes, including plus size: Higher BMI does not guard against dangerous heart risks. ScienceDaily. 6 November 2019. <www.sciencedaily.com/rel eases/2019/11/191106130340.htm>.

4. Golden NH, Mehler PS. Atypical anorexia nervosa can be just as bad. Cleve Clin J Med. 2020 Mar;87(3):172-174. doi: 10.3949/ccjm.87a.191 46. PMID: 32127441.

5. Harrop EN, Mensinger JL, Moore M, Lindhorst T. Restrictive eating dis- orders in higher weight persons: A systematic review of atypical anorexia nervosa prevalence and consecutive admission literature. Int J Eat Disord. 2021 Aug;54(8):1328-1357. doi: 10.1002/eat.23519. Epub 2021 Apr 17. PMID: 33864277; PMCID: PMC9035356.

6. Mack T, Sanchez-Roige S, Davis, LK. Genetic investigation of the contri- bution of body composition to anorexia nervosa in an electronic health record setting. Transl Psychiatry. 2022;486(12). https://doi.org/10.1038 /s41398-022-02251-y.

Chapter 7

Stop Denying the Signs of a Struggling Body

A key feature of a restrictive eating disorder, arising from the evolutionary flee-from-famine response, is the inability to recognise how physically depleted and at risk you are. Our ancestors who needed to keep moving to find an abundant foraging ground, wouldn't have made it far if they'd realised how much their body was struggling. Denial of their current physical state was critical to them staying determined and motivated enough to keep going. Today, this denial of how depleted and physically at risk you are is a trait that maintains your addictive compulsions.

There are several signs and symptoms that you very likely experience and ignore, trivialise or brush off as *normal,* but which are clear signs from your body that it's semi-starved and struggling. This is the case, no matter what your current body size.

Common Signs of a Struggling Energy-Deprived Body

- Feeling cold

- Hair loss

- Brittle hair and nails

- Dry skin

- Lanugo (fine hair covering the body)

- Constipation or diarrhoea

- Other digestive issues

- Nausea

- Food intolerances

- Heart palpitations and irregular heart rhythms

- Low heart rate (this is not a sign of fitness!)

- Poor circulation with a possible blue tinge to fingers and toes, with or without numbness

- Low blood pressure

- Low blood sugar

- Dizziness

- Vertigo

- Stumbling or reduced coordination

- Ear popping or ringing to the ears

- Headaches

- Shortness of breath

- Constant nervous energy

- Never getting sick

- Getting sick a lot

- No periods

- No sex drive

- Lethargy

- Poor sleep

- Frequent urination, especially at night

- Osteopenia or osteoporosis leading to stress fractures

- Dental problems, including gum recession, enamel erosion, cavities and loss of bone

- Anaemia

- Lack of emotions

You won't necessarily have all these symptoms but no matter how many you do or don't have, the fact you have some, is a sign that your body is struggling. Your brain will try to convince you that the symptoms you have *aren't that bad* but they are and they matter.

Your brain and body are doing all they can to keep you alive each and every day. That's their primary agenda and burying your head in the sand about how much your body is struggling won't change your reality.

Restrictive eating disorders are excellent at allowing you to live in a bubble of denial about how sick you are. You might even believe that you are more than just ok because you never get sick, you have more energy than most people you know and you keep going every day feeling *fine*. But you and I both know this is an illusion and neither your body nor your life are really *fine*. Some day your body won't have the ability to keep compensating for the stress it's under. So, before that day comes, do all you can to restore it and allow it to function for you as well as it can. The vast majority of the physical consequences listed above will reverse when you restore your body and get out of energy deficit. Unfortunately, bone density loss has less potential for repair if you are older than twenty-five years and some heart changes can be longer-lasting. Avoid adding to the burden on your body and it will do all it can to keep working for you.

Chapter 8

Physical Anomalies With Restrictive Eating Disorders

There are a few physical anomalies that can occur with restrictive eating disorders when you are still restricting and in energy deficit. These can reinforce the belief that you shouldn't be eating dense foods, resting or aiming to gain weight, although it's doing just those things that will correct them.

High Cholesterol

It's not uncommon for people with restrictive eating disorders to have high cholesterol levels. This can give rise to anxiety that you are eating the *wrong foods* and should restrict your fat intake further. However, following the typical (diet culture influenced, ahem) advice on how to lower cholesterol will only exacerbate your problem.

When I was heavily restricting, I had a cholesterol test as part of a so-called *well-being* check. My cholesterol was very high. I've since had a number of clients in the same position, anxious because they have high cholesterol and have even been advised by poorly informed health professionals to cut back on their fat intake or exercise more. If they did restrict or exercise more, their cholesterol would likely be the last of their concerns!

High cholesterol in people with restrictive eating disorders is very common. It's been found that people with anorexia nervosa have higher cholesterol levels than people who don't have restrictive eating disorders[1]. Nineteen to forty-eight percent of people with bulimia nervosa also have high cholesterol. It's also reported that total cholesterol, LDL and HDL levels can all be elevated (which are both the *good* and *bad* types of cholesterol)[2]. This anomaly is not fully understood but it's thought it could be due to genetic, hormonal and gut bacteria changes bought about by restrictive eating. In females, another key contributory factor is likely to be low oestrogen levels, also caused by the energy deficit state.

For the majority of people, eating more of all food types, removing restriction on fats and sugars and allowing your body to restore from energy deficit will allow your blood cholesterol levels to return to a normal level. The things you should not do are eat less, cut out fats, or exercise in an attempt to reduce it.

Anyone who hasn't had a cholesterol test, please don't go rushing out to get tested. It isn't necessary. Just let your body heal, restore and repair, while you also overcome the eating disorder on a brain-based level. This information is included here, not to encourage people to demand cholesterol tests, but to reassure anyone who has been tested and told their level is high that this is a normal anomaly found in people with restrictive eating disorders and everyone needs to keep eating.

Blood Sugar Changes

Hypoglycaemia or low blood sugar is something that many people experience with an active restrictive eating disorder, sometimes without symptoms. As you start to eat more in the process to overcome the eating disorder, episodes of reactive hypoglycaemia can also occur, especially in the earlier stages. This is when your body releases too much insulin in response to the food you have just consumed, causing your blood sugar to crash soon after eating.

Less commonly but commonly enough, people can also experience elevated blood sugar levels when they begin to eat more and their body is adjusting to the extra food intake. Unfortunately, this can be another anomaly that results in misleading advice. I've met more than one client who has been told by their primary care doctor that an elevated blood sugar test is an indication they have pre-diabetes. This is unlikely to be the case. Instead, these elevated blood sugar levels are a sign that your body is trying to adjust and establish what insulin response it needs to provide to a higher level of energy intake—something it hasn't been used to for a long time. If you keep eating without any form of restriction, your body will reach a level state again with an appropriate insulin response and levels of stored energy that ensure your blood sugar levels can remain consistent within a normal range.

Not Getting Sick

In well over a decade of having a restrictive eating disorder, I rarely got sick. And by sick, I mean colds, coughs, flu, tummy bugs and other infections or viruses. This is the case for many with eating disorders. Despite being very depleted, in a state of significant energy deficit and perhaps even exposed to people with viruses and colds, it's possible that you sail through without so much as a sniffle.

This is just another way in which an eating-disordered brain can then convince you that you aren't that depleted or malnourished, because the people around you who are supposedly *healthy*, are laid up with the flu, while you carry on feeling great.

Not getting sick is perhaps one of the biggest anomalies to a restrictive eating disorder because not only do you avoid infections and viruses when others don't, but it's likely you have a weakened immune system in comparison to *healthy* people, demonstrated when blood tests are taken. People with anorexia are often found to have low white blood cells, neutrophils and leukocytes, which are all key for our immune system, yet they rarely experience infectious illnesses[3]. Of course, that's not to say you won't or can't get sick with a restrictive eating disorder. You can and if you do, due to your weakened immune system, it's likely to be harder to shake off.

The reasons why people with restrictive eating disorders don't get sick in the same way *healthy* people do are not fully understood but one explanation that holds some credibility is that you are not a good host to the bacteria and viruses. Bacteria and viruses want lots of nutrients from your body to feed on and if you barely have sufficient supplies to keep yourself going, there isn't going to be as much available to these organisms in comparison to a well-nourished person.

But whatever the reason for this anomaly, your belief that you are super-human because you never get sick is very definitely false. Your body is not superhuman and neither are you. This is a sign that you are very depleted and more evidence that you are in a state of energy-deficit. When you do start to get colds, coughs and other viruses, you know that your body is heading in the right direction.

1. Hussain AA, Hübel C, Hindborg M, Lindkvist E, Kastrup AM, Yilmaz Z, Støving RK, Bulik CM, Sjögren JM. Increased lipid and lipoprotein concentrations in anorexia nervosa: A systematic review and meta-analysis. Int J Eat Disord. 2019 Jun;52(6):611-629. doi: 10.1002/eat.23051. Epub 2019 Mar 28. PMID: 30920679; PMCID: PMC6842568.

2. Tith RM, Paradis G, Potter BJ, et al. Association of bulimia nervosa with long-term risk of cardiovascular disease and mortality among women. JAMA Psychiatry. 2020;77(1):44–51. doi:10.1001/jamapsychiatry.2019.2914.

3. Słotwińska SM, Słotwiński R. Immune disorders in anorexia. Cent Eur J Immunol. 2017;42(3):294-300. doi: 10.5114/ceji.2017.70973. Epub 2017 Oct 30. PMID: 29204095; PMCID: PMC5708211.

Chapter 9

Period Talk
& Hypothalamic
Amenorrhoea

If you are a female of menstruating age, it's possible that the restrictive eating disorder has impacted your menstrual cycle and you have experienced what's known as *hypothalamic amenorrhoea* (HA). You might have a hit-and-miss, irregular cycle or you might not have had a period for some time, possibly years or decades. You might also think that not having a period isn't a big deal BUT your period and your hormonal health do matter.

With HA, your oestrogen levels are low. Low oestrogen affects your physical, mental and cognitive health and function in significant ways. Not all females with HA have eating disorders but it's understandable why a restrictive eating disorder can lead to HA when the three main causes are psychological stress, excessive exercise and disordered eating. It's also important to understand that HA can occur at any body size and weight. And for any of you who do still have a regular menstrual cycle, the presence of your period is not a sign of *health* in relation to the eating disorder or an indication of being out of energy deficit.

Two of the most significant physical consequences of HA are high cholesterol and loss of bone density. This creates a high risk of developing osteopenia or osteoporosis, even in young women. Most people with HA also find that they have a very low or even no libido, impacting their relationships with sexual partners[1].

You very likely already had some awareness of the physical risks of HA. The symptoms you might not have appreciated are the consequences of HA on your mental and cognitive health:

- Oestrogen influences a large number of brain regions which serve different but crucial functions, as well as affecting receptors for chemicals like serotonin, key in mood regulation. This means that low oestrogen can impact mood and behaviour.

- Where stress can lead to the development of HA, the relationship is reciprocal and low oestrogen also impacts on your stress levels. Women with HA experience more depression, greater anxiety and find it harder to cope with daily stress than those with a healthy menstrual cycle. Many women with HA also experience high levels of feeling insecure, inadequate and a sense of lack of control[2].

- It's not just general stress, depression and anxiety that can arise from low oestrogen. It can also give rise to a greater risk of affective disorders and post-traumatic stress disorder (PTSD). Fear extinction and being able to process traumatic events is more effective in women with high oestrogen than low, from which it's concluded that if you have chronically low oestrogen levels, you are at greater risk of adverse effects from trauma[3].

- Sleep too is affected by HA. Oestrogen improves the quality of your sleep, reduces time to fall asleep and increases time spent asleep. It also stops you from waking frequently in the night. And, of course, sleep is key for mood, productivity, alertness and cognitive function[4].

- Oestrogen also impacts memory and cognition (your thinking skills). It has a key role to play in enhancing your brain's neuroplasticity (its ability to rewire and adapt) which you need for all that important reprogramming. Women with higher oestrogen also have better attention and focus, improved planning ability and mental flexibility.

- And finally, although you might not be worried about this now, you should be; oestrogen protects your brain against inflammation, strokes later in life and other neurodegenerative disorders, including Alzheimer's as you age. Low oestrogen reduces this level of protection[5].

With all the effects oestrogen has on your health, it's hard to deny that establishing healthy oestrogen levels is crucial for current and long-term function. Whether you intend to have children or not, oestrogen is a critical hormone to maintain at a healthy level.

As stated above, HA can occur in anyone who exercises excessively, eats restrictively and/or is under a lot of stress. And the way to address it is the same as with overcoming the eating disorder. Stop exercise, eat without restriction, allow your body to emerge from energy deficit and reduce stress in your wider life wherever you can.

The thought of resuming your menstrual cycle might be difficult and if it is, remember that your brain, when you resume your periods and have more oestrogen flowing, will also be functioning better and you are likely to cope more easily than you can predict at the moment.

Overall, HA recovery gives you a chance to ensure healthy hormone function and all the benefits that come with it.

For anyone who uses contraceptive hormones or hormone replacement products and has a regular bleed—these bleeds aren't true periods or indicative of hormonal health

---

1. Shufelt CL, Torbati T, Dutra E. Hypothalamic amenorrhea and the long-term health consequences. Semin Reprod Med. 2017 May;35(3):256-262. doi: 10.1055/s-0037-1603581. Epub 2017 Jun 28. PMID: 28658709; PMCID: PMC6374026.

2. Albert K, Pruessner J, Newhouse P. Estradiol levels modulate brain activity and negative responses to psychosocial stress across the menstrual cycle. Psychoneuroendocrinology. 2015 Sep;59:14-24. doi: 10.1016/j.psyneuen.2015.04.022. Epub 2015 May 7. PMID: 26123902; PMCID: PMC4492530.

3. Glover EM, Jovanovic T, Norrholm SD. Estrogen and extinction of fear memories: implications for posttraumatic stress disorder treatment. Biol Psychiatry. 2015;78(3):178-185. doi:10.1016/j.biopsych.2015.02.007.

4. Tranoulis A, Georgiou D, Soldatou A, Triantafyllidi V, Loutradis D, Michala L. Poor sleep and high anxiety levels in women with functional hypothalamic amenorrhoea: A wake-up call for physicians? Eur J Obstet Gynecol Reprod Biol X. 2019 May;1. PMID: 31403123; PMCID: PMC6687383.

5. Brann DW, Dhandapani K, Wakade C, Mahesh VB, Khan MM. Neurotrophic and neuroprotective actions of estrogen: basic mechanisms and clinical implications. Steroids. 2007 May;72(5):381-405. doi: 10.1016/j.steroids.2007.02.003. Epub 2007 Feb 21. PMID: 17379265; PMCID: PMC2048656.

Chapter 10
Males & Sex Hormones

F or the male readers—your sex hormones will also be affected by restrictive eating and energy deficit. This matters for your health too.

As a result of energy deficit, your testosterone levels are likely to be lower than they should be, resulting in:

- a reduction in your muscle strength and mass;

- reduced bone density, especially if you are or have been affected by the eating disorder during puberty;

- a low libido;

- hypogonadism

- erectile dysfunction[1].

As with females, restoring your body to an energy-balanced state by addressing your restrictive eating, exercise and other compensatory behaviours to fully overcome the eating disorder, will allow your hormone levels to correct and normalise, so that these effects of insufficient hormones can resolve.

---

1. Skolnick A, Schulman RC, Galindo RJ, Mechanick JI. The endocrinopathies of male anorexia nervosa: Case series. AACE Clin Case Rep. 2016 Fall;2(4):e351-e357. doi: 10.4158/EP15945.CR. PMID: 28868357; PMCID: PMC5578418.

Chapter 11

Abstain from Restriction by Aiming for Overshoot

To overcome a restrictive eating disorder, you need to address the restrictive eating that led to its development and the eating habits that now maintain it. Your body needs to emerge from its current state of energy deficit and it's necessary to reprogram your brain from its addiction to the pursuit of energy deficit and associated behaviours. Without addressing these, you won't find freedom. If you have read the earlier sections of this book or *Addicted to Energy Deficit*, then you know that the best chance of achieving full freedom from the eating disorder is by aiming for overshoot. Abstaining from all restrictive eating is a crucial part of this.

The following chapters cover how to find the restriction in your eating habits and address it, recognising all the forms of hunger that you experience. There are also more tips to eating freely and abundantly.

Addicted to Energy Deficit explains why abstaining from all eating disorder behaviours, including restriction, is important for brain reprogramming. There is also information about how to abstain from restriction and the mindset that can help achieve this. To serve as a reminder or for anyone who has not read it, an abridged excerpt from *Addicted to Energy Deficit* about abstaining from restriction is given below. This will help you to contextualise the information provided in the coming chapters:

> *It's incredibly difficult to begin to understand what unrestricted eating looks like in someone coming out of an energy-deprived state. If you have eaten in restrictive and rigid ways for years then eating anything more, however small, feels extreme. To override this potential mental block, so that you can fully abstain from restrictive eating, you will need to reflect and prepare.*

> *One of the most effective ways of abstaining from all restriction is to take a step back and remove yourself from the scenario. Avoid allowing your emotional response to get in the way. Instead, imagine you are advising someone who needs to do the absolute opposite of eating as if they are on a diet. What would you advise them to do? What would Joe Bloggs on the street advise if this question was put to him?*

> *The answers that come to you will be exactly what you need to do to abstain from restriction.*

To eat in the opposite way to someone on a diet means eating all the time and predominantly high-fat, high-calorie foods. It's having big meals and lots of snacks. There would be no avoidance of processed or fast foods. Nothing should be avoided other than diet products. You wouldn't count calories or have limits.

If you keep asking yourself what a person who is doing the opposite to someone on a diet would do, someone wanting to GAIN weight (aiming for overshoot) then the answers will lead you to the action you need to take to abstain from restriction. The only right amounts to eat are as much as you can.

The other benefit to this approach is that it also addresses a lot of the smaller behaviours and rituals, such as only eating at certain times of the day. After all, if you were deliberately aiming for weight gain, removing any limits, why would you wait to eat?

Get into the aim to gain mindset and it will lead you to the exact things that you need to do to abstain from all restriction and restrictive behaviours.

Now you might be thinking, but I don't want to gain weight or I'm scared of gaining weight. In my experience, most people deal a lot better with weight gain than they think they will. And this approach is the best way to make sure you are abstaining from all the restrictive behaviours and habits that maintain the eating disorder's addictive nature. It's also the method that will enable your brain to fully unwire all the old circuits that drive the restrictive behaviours because you will no longer be using them, whilst wiring in circuits that will help you to create new habits related to unrestricted eating. Any resulting weight gain is a side effect of claiming your health and freeing your life.

A Few More Tips to Abstain from Restrictive Eating

As you pursue the abstinence approach, you might need a few more ground rules if you are struggling to get into the right mindset straight away. If this is the case then here are a few suggestions for some additional black-and-white rules to put in place:

– Set yourself a high baseline amount of food that you have to eat as a minimum every day no matter what.

– When setting your high baseline amount of food, a meal plan isn't necessary. Meal plans in themselves are frequently too restrictive and provide too much structure that then becomes fixed, rigid and hard to break. To set a high baseline amount, choose a method that works for you. Have a mental image of what your intake should be. You might work with a coach or a good dietician (someone who supports full unrestricted eating) to establish this.

– Eat to all hunger above your baseline. If you recognise any signs of hunger, whether they are physical, mental, emotional or behavioural then you should be eating. Not eating when your body is sending you hunger signals is restriction.

– When extreme hunger hits, let it take you as high as it needs to.

– Recognise the habitual ways in which you use restrictive behaviours in your day-to-day life, beyond the obvious.

– Learn to become very honest with yourself and with those supporting you. Whenever you finish eating something, ask yourself, could I eat more right now? If you could still be putting food in your mouth and physically eating then the answer is yes. Therefore, eat more.

– Abstain fully from restriction by taking on the aiming to gain mindset and aim for overshoot!

This abstinence approach, in which you act like a person fully intending to gain weight, can be easier to understand when you are starting and it's often more effective. With time, this approach will help you to relearn your body signals. The natural intuition of what hunger feels like, mentally and physically is more comprehensible when you have experienced what true satiety

feels like. When you reach this point, it's possible to continue the
process of fully abstaining from any restriction by beginning to
experiment with eating to hunger and appetite, using the signals
your brain and body are sending.

Excerpt from Addicted to Energy Deficit

Now that you have more context of the recommended abstinence approach, the next chapters explore the topics of restriction, hunger, food and eating in more depth.

Chapter 12

Weeding Out All Restriction

Y ou already know that the gold standard approach to fully overcome an eating disorder is to abstain from restriction and to aim for overshoot. It's necessary to address all forms of restriction, no matter how small, concerning how, what, when and with whom you eat. This isn't always easy when restrictive eating habits have become so ingrained and natural to you that they are now hard to identify for what they are.

Some of the ways that your restrictive habits might manifest can also be insidious, so the people around you won't appreciate that they are signs of restriction. It's often the case that loved ones or friends come to accept some of the eating disorder's habits as just your *little quirks*. This means that they don't challenge them because they consider them to be insignificant.

Let's be real though. The truth is that when overcoming a restrictive eating disorder, you could be eating thousands more calories, even ten to twenty thousand calories a day, appearing to be doing amazingly well at this game of aiming for overshoot and abstaining from restriction. But you could still be restricting. And that restriction can manifest in so many of the decisions that you make in the day, even decisions which on the surface don't appear to be food related.

It's therefore important that you can identify all the ways, however small and sneaky, that restriction appears in your daily life so that you can address them. Below are some of the common places that restriction can hide, even when you are eating huge amounts and facing *fear* foods like never before.

Where Restrictive Weeds Can Linger:

- **Eating to any limits**

This could be eating to a set number of calories in the day or to a meal plan. These limits, no matter how high, become barriers that you won't allow yourself to exceed, even if you're hungry for more. The limits can equally apply to macro or micronutrients, perhaps related to fat, sugar or carbohydrates. Any limits that you won't allow yourself to exceed are restrictive.

- **Limits on amounts you will eat of specific foods**

This could be the number of scoops or portions you will have of an item or weighing it to a certain limit.

- **Restricting how many times you will eat a specific food type**

Common examples of this are how many times you will let yourself have chocolate, white bread, ice cream or other sugary foods in a day or week. It can also manifest with meals, such as only allowing a certain type of meal once a week or less. For example, *I've already had pizza this week so can't again.*

- **Labelling foods by the time of day they can be eaten**

Having rules about what time of day you can eat certain food types and not allowing yourself to have them at other times is another way that an eating disorder can restrict you from eating what you want at the time you want it.

- **Comparing your intake today to yesterday or the same day a week ago**

This is where you compare to yesterday's intake, not allowing yourself to exceed it. This is common to an addicted brain needing a higher level of the *drug* to keep getting the same rewarding effects.

- **Only eating at certain times of day**

You might think that limiting your eating to certain times of the day is ok if you are eating more than you used to and facing foods that you haven't for years at the times you do eat. However, if you can't let yourself eat at other times then it's a problem. It can also be torturous if you are hungry but won't let yourself eat until the next permitted time. Waiting to eat despite hunger is a definite form of restriction.

- **Only eating in certain locations, with particular people or if you have a reasonable amount of time to do so**

Any limits on where you will eat, who with and how need to be addressed. Your brain needs to learn that you can eat anywhere, alone or with others and that you can eat even if you only have two minutes to force something down before an appointment. Food is never off limits and you need to overcome any beliefs that every eating experience needs to be perfect.

- **Delaying eating**

Food is precious when you are in energy deficit and continuing to eat with restriction. This creates a drive to delay eating so that you still have it to look forward to before you fall into bed at night. But delaying eating is pure restriction because food is available without limits, day and night.

- **Weighing or measuring foods**

People with eating disorders can become very attached to their kitchen scales and weigh out anything and everything. If you are eating without limits then you don't need to measure food. You eat as much as you want of whatever it is and keep eating it until your brain and body say, *I'm done with that now but quite fancy x instead*, and then you have that. Scales are machines of restriction. Dispose of them.

- **Calorie and number checking**

Calorie and number checking or tracking is another weapon of restriction and reinforces habits of only eating to a certain limit or making your food choices based on what the numbers say. Calorie counting can be a hard habit to break but you can break it. Avoid looking at the numbers and if you do see them, go high (see Chapter 28).

- **Not buying the foods that you want to avoid having them at home**

When out shopping, you might subconsciously avoid buying the less restrictive foods because of thoughts that, if you don't have them at home then you won't be able to eat them. You need to fill your cupboards at home with the least restrictive options so that you don't have the, *I don't have any,* excuse not to eat the things you are really hungry for.

- **Matching how much you eat to a partner/parent/sibling/friend, only eating when they do**

Matching your intake to someone else and not letting yourself eat more than them will maintain restrictive eating habits because when emerging from a state of energy deficit, your body needs a lot more food than someone with an energy-balanced appetite. Your true appetite is likely to be extremely high. You need to learn to respond to it no matter what other people are or aren't doing.

- **Special diet restrictions**

If you need a special diet for genuine medical or other non-eating disorder-related reasons, this isn't aimed at you. This point refers to those who choose a special diet, such as avoiding meat, animal products, wheat, dairy or other things, not because of a true (and I mean true) medical need to avoid them or because of real ethical beliefs but because the eating disorder has created powerful stories over the years as to why these foods should be restricted.

- **The small ways restriction can manifest:**

  - eating bread, even lots of bread, but not buttering it;

  - eating 3 big magnums when you really want 5 or 6;

  - choosing one flavour of ice cream over another because it has 13 less calories;

  - having the big milky drink but saying no to the cream or toppings;

  - avoiding the higher calorie sauces or dressings with a meal;

  - having a pear instead of a banana because, despite eating thousands of calories in a day now, bananas are still a fear;

  - eating a *fear food*, such as a huge sandwich with loads of cheese and butter but not having the crisps you really want with it.

All of these things count. Notice every decision when it comes to food and where the restriction lingers.

- **Diet products of any type**

Diet products are pure restriction when you are deliberately aiming to eat unrestrictedly. Full-fat and full-sugar options always taste better.

- **Pre or post-event restriction**

This is restricting before an event or big meal to give yourself *permission to eat* later, or restricting afterwards as a way to compensate, even though you are still bloody hungry. You don't need to restrict as permission to eat later or after a huge feast. To overcome the eating disorder and fully reprogram your brain, it's important that you don't.

- **Restriction in response to weight gain**

Many people restrict, perhaps unconsciously, if they notice their weight has gone up and judge it to be too fast or inappropriate. This can be because weight gain has been a strong trigger to your eating disorder habits and so the old pathways are fired up when you notice a weight increase. If you notice this, you need to address it. Being free of the eating disorder means letting go of any attempts to manipulate your body weight and shape (see Chapter 27).

- **Ignoring cravings**

You are still restricting if you aren't responding to what your body and brain are guiding you towards. Recognise what you want to eat, no matter how bizarre, terrifying or unhealthy you perceive it to be. Those cravings are coming from a body that knows what it needs for optimal health and restoration.

- **Using compensatory behaviours as a form of restriction**

This could be exercising as a way to restrict your intake because it has the effect of blunting or distracting you from your appetite or to compensate for what you have eaten. All compensatory behaviours are a means to make up for eating or to give you permission to eat more later and hence an indirect form of restriction.

- **Keeping busy**

Keeping busy, whether mentally or physically, is very often used by people with restrictive eating disorders as a way to avoid eating or hunger and it's a form of restriction. Aim to rest and relax much more, let the hunger in and respond to it.

This list is a starting point of some of the ways that restrictive weeds can linger. Use these examples and reflect on where the restrictive behaviours and habits linger for you, also identifying others beyond this list.

All ongoing restriction that continues to sneak in matters. Find where restriction lingers, weed it out and destroy it. Even if you are eating tons more at the moment and only restricting now in small ways, those small restrictive habits that remain will be continuing to reinforce to your brain that you can eat too much, that numbers matter and that times of day or who you are eating with make a difference.

These restrictive habits might not make a difference to whether you weight restore or gradually emerge from energy deficit but they do keep the eating-disordered brain network firing up and give rise to more dopamine spikes. This will impact on your ability to successfully achieve the brain reprogramming needed to find full freedom.

Chapter 13

Additional Tips to Abstain from All Restriction

O nce you have reflected on all the ways that you are restricting, you can address it.

Chapter 11 reiterated some of the advice included in *Addicted to Energy Deficit* about how to approach abstinence from restriction. This chapter provides you with some additional tips to increase your likelihood of success with bashing out your restrictive habits.

Abstaining from All Restriction

1. If you have hunger... EAT

Respond to all hunger. Identify your hunger signals, using the information provided in Chapter 15 and respond with food.

2. Choose the densest options and the path of <u>most</u> resistance

Eating more but playing it safe with what you eat is restriction. It won't help you to address the ongoing resistance to certain food types and fully reprogram your brain.

3. Address any food rules or restrictive urges as soon as you notice them

If in any doubt that the choice you are making is restrictive, assume it is and choose something that you know isn't.

4. Remind yourself that your body needs all the energy it can get

If you have been restricting at any level for any amount of time, then no matter what your weight or BMI, your body is hungry and in a state of energy deficit. It needs energy, nutrients and fats to establish energy balance and until it does, you can't fully overcome the eating disorder.

5. Apply the, *What would pre-eating disorder me have eaten?* question

The foods you ate before the eating disorder started or your childhood favourites are usually still foods that you will enjoy now if you let yourself eat them. Start eating them again.

6. Don't save calories for later

This is textbook eating disorder behaviour. Eat any time, responding to all hunger.

7. Deliberately eat every half an hour

One tool you can use is to deliberately eat every half an hour or every hour to remove any time of day rules or delaying habits. If you do this, ensure each eating event is also significant. And if you have hunger before the half hour is up, don't wait.

8. Remind yourself that unrestricted eating will feel very wrong but is right

Eating without restriction is likely to feel wrong and chaotic but that's exactly why you need to do it. Eating should never feel wrong—it's not a normal human reaction. It's purely created by an eating disorder. Eat despite the feelings of wrong-doing and very soon, eating will only feel right and good.

9. Label eating disordered thoughts as irrelevant, flick them away and eat

Thoughts generated by the eating disorder will be constant and may initially be stronger as you eat with less restriction. Let the thoughts arise but label them as eating disordered and irrelevant. Then flick them away while grabbing more food.

10. Expect negative emotions, label them as inappropriate and keep eating

Feelings of greed, guilt, shame and self-disgust are also to be expected when eating with less restriction. Expect these emotions, label them as powerful attempts by your brain to keep you in a state of energy deficit and, as with the thoughts above, flick them away while continuing to eat with no restriction.

11. Address compensatory behaviours

Exercise, purging, laxatives, diet pills or chewing and spitting behaviours are all forms of restriction. Seek support to address them.

12. Avoid keeping constantly busy (mentally and/or physically)

Staying busy is often a form of restriction and a way to avoid hunger and eating. Allow space in your life for everything that overcoming an eating disorder entails. Let the hunger in and keep your focus on true unrestricted eating and all that means for you.

13. Repeatedly remind yourself you cannot treat a restrictive eating disorder with restriction

14. Remember that diet foods taste terrible compared to the real deal
No more diet foods. Stop buying them, stop giving money to the diet industry—it's rich enough. Be grateful that you don't have to eat that rubbish again.

15. Feel mentally and emotionally exhausted but do it anyway
Keep reminding yourself that overcoming any addiction and not least an eating disorder will never feel comfortable but you can feel rubbish and do it anyway. The more you do, the sooner you stop feeling so mentally and emotionally drained and find you can eat without restriction and feel good about it.

16. Eat foods in their least restrictive forms, always erring on the side of caution
Add butter to bread, full-fat milk to coffee/tea and cream to anything. Choose large wherever possible and always make the least restrictive food choices that are available to you. No level of restriction should feature in anything you consume.

17. If you are thinking of food or dreaming of ice cream, then eat them now, not delaying until later.

18. Eaten a huge meal and still hungry? Don't judge it. Eat more
Eating more is never wrong but not eating despite hunger is restriction.

19. Don't judge what and how much you want to eat. Just listen to your body
No matter how much food your body is asking for or what that food is, don't judge it, just follow it.

20. Delete the trackers and ditch the food scales or other measuring devices

Eating without restriction is not measurable. Only your body can tell you what it needs in terms of food quantity.

21. Use some little mind games to change your perception:

- When you are doubting a decision, ask yourself what you'd advise a friend who was overcoming a restrictive eating disorder in this moment. Detach from yourself and follow the advice you know you'd give to someone else.

- When faced with food options, apply the question, *If all food was zero calories, what would I choose right now?* It's amazing how many times the answer is burger or cake and not lettuce or kale.

- Aim to live the life you want tomorrow today. Eat today all the things you want to be able to eat in your future life. Until you do, that tomorrow won't ever arrive.

- Apply the *opposite actions* mindset. If your brain is telling you not to eat the Mars bar and eat the rice cracker instead, you eat the Mars bar. If your brain is telling you to just have the small fries, go large.

- Stay in the moment. Don't let worry about earlier or later affect what you eat now. We could be hit by a meteor later and all that angst would be over nothing.

22. Use your life values to guide you

Do you value diet culture, being thin and super fit according to society's misguided culture above anything? Or do you have values that are aligned with being happy, loving, free-minded, generous, fun and relaxed? Values that don't align with all that the eating disorder will allow you to be? Focus on your values and use them to make the right choices when it comes to how and what you eat and your determination to keep aiming for overshoot.

23. Fast or slow - ensure you make progress

Whether you go fast, *slam on the gas* style and eat all you crave, blasting through every bit of restriction or resistance to certain foods as you do or whether you go stepwise into addressing restriction is your choice. Just make sure you make progress and address everything.

24. Ensure any meal plans are always your minimum

If you are using a meal plan then please see it as a MINIMUM and never your maximum. Don't let a plan be a tool to restrict and if it is then it needs to be reviewed and a new approach found.

25. Eat foods prepared by others

Eat out and eat foods that someone else prepares so that it loosens your control over what you eat or how it's prepared. This is taking control back from the eating disorder. You might experience inner resistance to doing so, but that's why you need to do it.

26. Buy foods of unknown energy values

If you are calorie conscious then buy foods of unknown energy values. Find the foods without labels.

27. STOP buying diet, low calorie, low carb, low sugar or low-fat foods

Ben and Jerry's, NOT Halo Top!

28. Make a list of your fear foods and situations and face as many a day as you can

29. Repeat, repeat, repeat. Persistence is key

30. Deliberately eat more than others to rewire any old habits or beliefs that you can only eat as much as or less than other people

You are overcoming a restrictive eating disorder and your body needs are very different to someone who is energy-balanced.

31. Make yourself eat more than you thought you could

Examples might be ice cream by the tub (not scoops), huge large chocolate bars, family-sized bags of crisps and going XL in everything. Show yourself that you don't have to stop at a small or what is considered a single serving size. Abundance is your ticket out of restriction and out of the scarcity mindset (see Chapter 34).

32. Big challenge days

Shake things up regularly with days where you deliberately aim to eat everything in sight in deliberate big ways. This can be an excellent way to force yourself out of restrictive tendencies, show you what eating without any restriction can look like and help you continue eating with much less restriction, knowing you can and that any anxiety from doing so is inappropriate.

33. Bring games into the process

Find other ways to make the process of overcoming the eating disorder more of a game. Keep it interesting so you stay mentally engaged and don't become complacent or bored. This might be with challenge days—how many different bakery items can I eat today or eating Chinese or Italian food all day. Use others to help you plot and plan for this or ask them to join in to keep it even more engaging and spicy (see Chapter 69 on the importance of fun!).

34. Accept that the discomfort about weight gain might be there

The discomfort about gaining weight will never go unless it's faced. Eat, gain weight and learn that not only does the world not end when you do but a whole lot of things get a million times better.

35. Remember weight gain alone doesn't equate to being fully out of energy deficit or a re-programmed brain

Just because you have gained weight or hit some arbitrary target weight set by an eating disorder treatment team, remind yourself that this is about your mental state and not weight. If you still have fears around food, about eating without restriction or resistance to gaining more weight which are driving you to continue to engage in disordered thoughts or behaviours, then you have to keep focused, no matter what. Mental state, not weight!

36. Reflect each evening on where restriction appeared that day

Quietly sit each evening and go back over your day, identifying where any restriction appeared. This way you can address it.

37. Recognise the positives in each day

Each day, notice the positives and wins, however small. Find the good in the process. There will be plenty if you look. Recognise the wins and celebrate them, ideally with chocolate and cake.

38. Find and utilise your support team

Recovery in isolation might well be impossible and if not impossible at least one hundred times harder. Ask others to help, whether they are friends, family, a coach, a professional or ideally a whole team of people. Use them to support, cheerlead, keep you focused, stop you getting complacent and hold you accountable. This is a long journey. Without support, it's easy to burn out and lose momentum and motivation.

39. Accept your perceptions of what a lot of food is might be skewed

People who have been eating restrictively for a significant amount of time often have a skewed perception about what a lot of food looks like. This can lead you to eat just a couple more biscuits or a chocolate bar in the day and believe yourself to be eating so much food and *recovery amounts*. When this happens, detach from yourself for a moment and consider whether you'd think it a lot of food for somebody else. Then go back to the old mantra that if you are thinking of food then you are hungry and you need to be eating, no matter what came before.

40. Remember that if you don't fight then the eating disorder stays

Overcoming an eating disorder is exhausting and draining. It's easy to become mentally and emotionally burnt out in the process. It's a constant battle to stay on track 24/7 because there are no days off. But if you don't keep going, pushing the restrictive urges away, choosing the least restrictive option instead, then the eating disorder won't go anywhere fast. Fight and feel sh*t but know that the feeling will pass.

And a final bonus tip is to treat every day as if it's your first day in this process, no matter how much weight you've gained or how far you think you've come. Eat every day as if you are just starting out and until there are no doubts the eating disorder is gone.

Chapter 14

Eating Despite Low (Perceived) Appetite

To overcome a restrictive eating disorder it's essential to fully emerge from energy deficit. This means that, like it or not, you need to eat more food each day to not only meet your body's daily energy need but consistently exceed it. Therefore, appetite or not, it's important that you continue to eat enough to ensure you give your body the full amount of energy it needs. At times you are going to need to push yourself to eat, even if doing so feels mentally wrong, physically uncomfortable and distressing.

The title of this section includes the word *perceived* in relation to low appetite because when you are in energy deficit, your body is hungry, whether you can recognise this or not. The next chapter describes all the ways hunger can manifest, including the behavioural and emotional symptoms that are insidious signs of hunger. This chapter is about how to eat despite a low perceived appetite when you are overcoming a restrictive eating disorder, part of which is to recognise that just because your belly hunger or even your mental hunger isn't high, doesn't mean you don't have an appetite.

Low Appetite & Overcoming an Eating Disorder

The phenomenon of *extreme hunger* gets a lot of discussion within eating disorder recovery communities. The insatiable drive to eat that can kick in when you begin to eat more can be frightening, especially when people around you have never experienced it and you understand very little about what's happening or why your hunger is taking you to levels that feel out of control. It can all feel very wrong with a brain that's simultaneously still trying to pull you towards energy deficit and restriction. It's therefore understandable that extreme hunger is a common topic amongst those going through it or preparing for the possibility.

There's a lot less discussion about the low or even no appetite end of the hunger spectrum. Despite this, it's something that you are very likely to experience as your appetite swings to extremes and it can be just as unsettling and confusing as the insatiable hunger.

Low appetite when you aim to abstain from restriction is hard because it's then that you need to make yourself eat, even if you feel physically unwell or completely turned off by food.

You know what you *should* or need to eat but making yourself continue to do so when you feel physically stuffed full, bloated or even nauseous is when eating to overcome an eating disorder loses any appeal.

Low physical appetite is common at the early stage of the process when your stomach is getting used to more food but it can also show up at other times and each time it hits, it can be equally uncomfortable—physically, mentally and emotionally. At various stages of the process, another common scenario can be not only a loss of physical hunger but also reaching a point where food becomes less interesting or exciting.

Below are some of the ways in which low appetite can manifest at different stages in the process of overcoming an eating disorder and the common reasons for each.

Appetite as You Begin to Abstain from Restrictive Eating

It's very possible that habitual restrictive eating has left you with blunted hunger signals which need to be stimulated with food into reliable and consistent signs. This happens for several reasons:

1. Eating restrictively for some time has caused your stomach capacity to shrink and you have what's called slow gastric emptying. This means that it takes longer than it should for food to leave your stomach and process through your intestinal system. You may have constipation and eating more can lead to cramps and stomach spasms as your stomach also adjusts to new food types. All of this creates a perfect blend of early satiation, bloating, gas and low physical appetite. But that doesn't mean that your body isn't also very hungry.

2. When your food intake became restrictive at the beginning of the eating disorder, it's likely that your brain and body tried desperately to keep sending you hunger signals to drive you to eat more. When your intake remained low despite this hunger, your brain will have perceived that continuing to send those signals was futile. Creating and sending hunger signals is an energy intensive process and a body in energy deficit needs to preserve all the energy it can so won't waste precious resources if it doesn't lead to beneficial results.

3. Blunted hunger signals as a response to prolonged energy deficit are also thought to be a survival mechanism. In our ancestor's hunter-gatherer times, when being hungry was common if food was scarce in the environment, it was important that those affected could focus on finding food for their basic survival. If the hunger they were experiencing left them feeling constantly famished and what we call *hangry* (anger created by being overly hungry), then our ancestors would have been too distracted by their hunger to get on with finding the food they desperately needed. In their case, the hunger would be blunted while they found and gathered food but once they began to feast, it would reawaken their natural hunger cues. This survival mechanism was a useful short-term measure. It's not something that evolved for people with restrictive eating disorders today who are restricting their food intake despite abundant food availability.

When you begin the process of abstaining from restriction, you might need to do so despite low or no appetite. This particularly relates to physical appetite but your mental hunger might also be affected.

This is when you have to eat to stimulate your appetite.

When you start to eat more, despite little or no appetite, it will give your hunger a poke into life. For some people, this appetite reawakening can happen gradually and for others, it can be sudden and dramatic. Either way, eating can bring on the hunger. This is because increased food consumption tells your brain that food is available in your environment and so sending you signals to continue to eat could now result in you eating more of the foods it's desperate for.

In summary, whether you are just starting the process of overcoming the eating disorder or whether you have been *doing recovery* in a less restrictive but still restrictive way for a while, you need to eat more to stimulate your appetite to its true, high level.

Your Appetite Throughout the Process

Overcoming a restrictive eating disorder is a lengthy process. Even if you do jump into full abstinence to get your body out of energy deficit more rapidly and reprogram your brain more effectively, it can still take a year or more to reach a state of complete mental and physical healing.

During this time it's natural that your hunger will be up and down. This can be for many reasons, some of which you might be able to identify but others you won't. There are many occasions when your body will be working away to do internal repairs on all your tissues and organs and when this creates higher energy demands, all you will know is that you are more hungry than last week, probably more exhausted too. This is when it's necessary to learn to trust your body and follow the signals it's sending without overthinking or questioning them.

Hyperphagia, or what's commonly referred to as *extreme hunger,* is very likely to come and go throughout the process. Don't question it when it does and instead let it guide you. In times when the extreme hunger is not quite so extreme, stay mindful of the need to continue to eat good amounts of food, ensuring that your intake doesn't drop to a restrictive level again.

Unfortunately, you are also guaranteed to experience symptoms that make eating that bit harder. This can include days of feeling nauseous, acid reflux, severe bloating, cramps, spasms, constipation or diarrhoea. All these symptoms can occur as your stomach adjusts to processing more food again and food types it might not have digested for some time. These symptoms can make the thought of putting more food in your belly harder, but keep going. If your intake drops then you risk further energy deficit and triggering the addictive cravings and thoughts you are working so hard to overcome.

Due to how lengthy the process of overcoming a restrictive eating disorder is, you are likely to also have periods when you feel fed up and bored of having to keep eating so much. You will need to constantly check in with yourself that you are pushing in all directions against old restrictive habits. The initial days of abstaining from restriction can be exhilarating when you allow yourself to eat foods that have been off limits for so long but once this exhilaration wears off and the grind of the process sets in, it does get tough. When this happens you might believe that your mental hunger has reduced because the thought of eating more is less enticing and if this is coupled with a drop in physical hunger, you can perceive that your appetite has reduced when it hasn't. It's times like this that a shake-up of your approach can help to keep it interesting and ensure you stay engaged.

Your Appetite Towards The End of the Process

In the latter stages of the process, when you have physically restored an energy-balanced state, your appetite will naturally reduce and the days of extreme hunger will end.

Extreme hunger reduces in parallel with the full restoration of both fat and lean tissue stores to your body's set point. Fat overshoot is almost certainly a requirement to achieve this. This was discussed in more detail in *Addicted to Energy Deficit*. Therefore, your hunger levels will reduce as you reach your set point weight and allow for overshoot. However, this can also be a dangerous time. At this point, you are still developing the skill of being able to recognise your true hunger cues and trust your body. It's all too easy to be led astray by lingering eating disordered thoughts which still seek a return to feel-good hits created by energy deficit. This can manifest as thoughts about wanting to lose a tiny bit of weight or convincing yourself that you are less hungry now because your extreme hunger has gone, resulting in an unintentional return to some level of restrictive eating.

It's at this point that you are going to need to be very self-aware and vigilant, questioning the motivation behind any thoughts to eat less than you have become used to. People who have come out of energy deficit and overcome restrictive eating disorders tend to have extremely high energy needs for a long time after reaching an energy-balanced state. This means you will still need to keep your intake high, especially when compared to others of your sex and age.

What Do You Do If You Have NO Appetite?

I don't doubt that you have heard the advice that to recover from an eating disorder, you should respond to all your mental and physical hunger. In doing so your hunger will drive you to eat a significant amount of food, enable you to break your restrictive habits and guide you to mental and physical freedom.

But what if you don't think that you have any mental or physical hunger signs? Does this mean that you just don't eat until you do?

We both know that you won't get very far if you stop eating for long periods because you don't *feel* hungry. This whole process might not even get off the ground if you do only eat when hunger signals strike.

So yes, you do have to eat, even if you have a low appetite or you perceive yourself to have no appetite and even if you are feeling sick and unwell. But you can eat, appetite or not and keep aiming for overshoot. It will be worth it for the life it brings you.

How to Keep Eating Despite Low (*Perceived*) Appetite

Continuing to eat is hard when you have or believe yourself to have a low appetite. Some tips are given below on how to keep eating despite a low appetite so that you can remain steadfast in your pursuit of abstinence from all restrictive eating.

But first, remember that hunger comes in all forms. If you only respond to physical hunger then you won't be eating without restriction. This means that you won't wire in new brain circuits to drive unrestricted eating and you won't fully overcome the eating disorder, even if you are eating more than you were.

Three more things to be aware of when it comes to your appetite are:

1. Anxiety reduces your natural appetite.

2. Stress reduces your natural appetite.

3. Exercise, because it puts your body under stress, reduces your natural appetite.

Develop tools to reduce your anxiety and stress levels, relax as much as possible and avoid all unnecessary exercise to allow your natural appetite can come through.

Tips to Keep Eating with a Low Appetite:

1. Remind yourself that your body is hungry, whether you feel it or not. A body in energy deficit is hungry and needs food. Eating without an

appetite might create mental and physical discomfort but you really do need this food to find freedom from the eating disorder.

2. Recognise all forms of hunger even when your physical hunger is absent or you feel physically full or unwell. Use the information given in the next chapter to recognise when you are hungry. And when it comes to mental hunger, remind yourself that a brain that is satiated doesn't guide you to food thoughts. It finds other more interesting things to think about and do. Therefore, if your brain is guiding you to food, it's for a reason and you need to eat.

3. Keep to that baseline minimum amount of food that you eat every single day, no matter what your appetite is, but also keep striving to exceed it and go as high as your hunger takes you above it.

4. When you have any inkling of hunger, eat as soon as it hits, no matter what time of day or night it is. The more you can do this, the sooner your body will trust that sending you hunger signals is a worthwhile exercise because you are finally responding. Then your true appetite will come through.

5. When your hunger is low, aim for energy-dense foods. Yes, these will be the ones that create more anxiety but that's kind of the point. Eat highly dense but low-volume foods, such as ice creams, proper chocolate, chips, doughnuts and cheese, and add butter, oil and creams to things. Do all you can to add energy to what you are eating without adding bulk so that your body still gets the energy it so desperately needs. This will then help to stimulate your appetite and help your digestion.

6. Avoid the filler, bulky, fibrous foods that your restrictive urges love but your belly doesn't, especially when you need to be consuming so much more in terms of energy, fat and other dense foods in this process. This means avoiding lots of fruit, veggies and cereals that are all bulky,

harder to digest and have very little true energy value to them.

7. Recognise that anxiety, exercise and stress all cause low physical appetite because they put your body into stress response mode, releasing more adrenaline which is an appetite suppressant. This is a basic survival response because a stressed person needs to prioritise escaping the danger that's causing the stress, not sitting down and eating. Unfortunately when your stress and anxiety are triggered by food then sitting down and eating are exactly what you need to do despite the blunted appetite to ensure that food becomes less terrifying in future and you no longer have a stress response when you look at a doughnut.

8. Exercise kills your appetite for the same reasons stress and anxiety do. To the caveman brain, the reason a person would be running or engaging in significant exercise is to escape danger, so exercise puts the body back into adrenaline-pumping, stress response mode, blunting your appetite. You should be abstaining from exercise anyway and you will find that if you allow yourself to sit down, rest and relax, using anxiety-lowering tools if you need to, your appetite will likely come through.

9. Use hot water bottles, belly massages and wear elasticated waists. Deploy all the good old tools to help you when you are feeling physically stuffed, bloated or have stomach cramps... and then keep eating!

10. As explained, hunger often needs to be pushed into life at the start. Therefore, if your appetite remains low, eat more, focusing on energy-dense foods to give your body and brain the message that the famine is over and food is available. Fuel the hunger fire, using food to ignite it. If your hunger drops at any point, take a step back and reflect on whether your intake has dropped and become restrictive again, even in small ways. It's surprising how a small amount of increased energy deficit can cause the body to go back into survival mode, switching off true hunger signals once again. It never hurts to eat more to see what

it does to your appetite.

11. If food has become less exciting or enticing, it's probably because you have allowed yourself to fall into a rut of what and when you eat, even if it's much more than before. Make sure that your process is constantly evolving and take the time to reflect on what you are eating now and where the resistance still lies. Then shake things up again with what you eat, where, when or how. Ensure that you are constantly facing new challenges and foods to keep moving forward. When you do this, food will be a lot more interesting to your brain again.

12. And finally ... Grab hold of that *feck it* attitude and decide, *I might not think I'm hungry and my belly might be sore, but I'm going to blast this eating disorder out of my life with more food anyway!*

Overcoming a restrictive eating disorder means forcing yourself to eat when you don't feel like eating and even if you feel physically unwell. If you want to find your freedom and stay there, this is a skill you need to develop expertise in.

Hunger can be a luxury when you are abstaining from restriction. If you have it, let it take you as far as it will. But when the hunger isn't there, you don't get to eat less or not eat. Eat as much as you can, no matter what, or those addictive cravings will spark back into life and you will spiral back into higher levels of restrictive eating before you know it.

Chapter 15

Recognise All The Signs of Hunger

H unger signals can be very confusing when you have an eating disorder. Physical hunger can be blunted and you have likely avoided recognising and responding to other more subtle signs of hunger while your focus has been on the pursuit of energy deficit.

When you go through the process to overcome the eating disorder, you will need to tune into all your hunger signals so that you can respond to them and abstain from restriction. At times these hunger signals will be physical and your mental hunger is likely to be strong. However, the depth of your current hunger will also be evident in your behaviours and emotions.

Hunger in People Without Eating Disorders

Before considering hunger in someone with a restrictive eating disorder, it's helpful to identify how someone without a history of disordered eating experiences hunger. Because everyone (eating disorder or not) experiences, not just physical, but also mental hunger and some behavioural and emotional signs.

For most people, *mental hunger* or a change in how they are feeling emotionally is the only signal they need to guide them towards food. It's just rarely labelled as such.

People with normal hunger signals and non-disordered eating rarely reach the point of stomach growling physical hunger before they decide to eat again. Instead, when their brain notices that their energy levels are dropping, it will generate conscious thoughts of, *I'm feeling a bit peckish,* resulting in them going to grab a sandwich and Mars bar before returning to what they were doing. If they ignore these initial mental hunger signs, they might start to feel irritable or low as the next signal from their brain to eat and feel better.

What Happens to Hunger With a Restrictive Eating Disorder?

When you first entered a state of energy deficit, your brain will have increased your hunger signals to guide you to eat. You will have experienced increased physical signals so that you felt hunger in the sense of a stomach growling or empty belly sensation; mental signals, such as increasing thoughts about food to the point that you couldn't think about much else; emotional signs, such as feeling *hangry,* or behavioural ones, such as a strong urge to get access to food above anything else. Once your brain had been sending these signals for a time, without getting the results it wanted because you continued to eat restrictively and/or compensate, it will have stopped generating them because that in itself is an energy-consuming process. This is when your natural hunger became blunted and why any hunger signals you still get are less reliable.

As you overcome the eating disorder and abstain from restriction, your brain will gradually be able to trust that the perceived *famine* is now over and that it can send hunger signs because you will now respond.

Unfortunately though, while you remain in a state of energy deficit and until you have restored your fat and lean tissue stores to your unique set weight, your physical hunger signals will be inconsistent and unreliable. For this reason, you need to recognise and rely on your mental, emotional and behavioural hunger signs. Even with these, it's important to be aware that if you have been restricting for a long time, your mental hunger might also be suppressed as you have ignored even these attempts by your brain to make you eat. Let's face it, if you have spent many years eating habitual and rigid amounts to the clock, despite what your brain was asking for, then it's unlikely to immediately turn on reliable physical or mental hunger signals just because you have decided that today you are done with the eating disorder.

Happily, consistently eating more and aiming for overshoot will spark your hunger fully into life. In the meantime, you can use the emotional and behavioural signs that I don't doubt are present as clear evidence that you are hungry.

Listed below are some of the mental, physical, emotional and behavioural signs that you are hungry, even if the side of your brain that remains addicted to energy deficit tries to persuade you otherwise.

Physical Hunger Signs

These are some of the physical hunger signals that your body will send, beyond the commonly accepted ones such as stomach grumbling or an empty stomach sensation:

- feeling cold;

- physical shaking or trembling;

- becoming sweaty or clammy;

- feeling nauseous;

- headaches;

- dizziness or vertigo;

- poor balance;

- feeling faint;

- not sleeping well—your brain is trying to keep you awake to eat;

- sleeping a lot—your brain is trying desperately to preserve the energy it does have;

- feeling lethargic or exhausted;

- conversely to the above, feeling jittery and a constant urge to move—caused by the evolutionary migratory response;

- strong sugar cravings—a sign that your body is in need of instant energy;

- thirst, which can be a sign of hunger.

Mental Hunger Signs

Most people think of mental hunger as your brain's attempt to guide you to eat by obsessing about food or even obsessing over avoiding food, even when your belly feels full. Below are other common ways in which mental hunger can manifest:

- noticing what other people are eating and being hyperaware of food;

- dreaming about food or eating;

- lusting after foods you have avoided for years, whether you now let yourself eat them or not;

- mental gymnastics over what, when and how to eat, who to eat with and what you will eat later;

- food taking a higher priority in your life than it should and a desire for food to be perfect;

- being hyper-aware and sensitive to diet culture topics and messages;

- poor ability to concentrate, for example on reading, TV and conversations;

- conversely to the above, feeling mentally very sharp, probably too sharp—a sign that your brain is hyper-vigilant as a result of hunger;

- asking yourself if you are hungry or not;

- obsessing over meal plans and ruminating about them;

- ruminating on how much you have eaten that day;

- asking yourself or others if the food you have eaten or plan to eat is *enough* or *too much;*

- food obsessions and cravings;

- wondering if you should eat now or later, what you will eat or ruminating over how to avoid eating more;

- finishing a meal or snack and having an instant urge to eat more;

- beliefs that there are right and wrong ways and amounts to eat and you have to do what is *right*.

The next lists provide some of the ways that hunger can manifest within your emotions and behaviours. You could argue that these are symptoms of hunger that fall into the mental or physical categories and I'd agree that the lines are blurry. But it can be helpful to recognise how much hunger impacts your emotions and behaviours, not focusing solely on your thoughts and physical symptoms.

Emotional Hunger Signs

Hunger commonly manifests in our emotions. A well-recognised symptom of hunger is that of being *hangry*, which is to feel angry or irritable when you need to eat. Because your brain is focused on survival, it will create some wacky emotions when your body is in a state of energy deficit because this is a potentially life-threatening situation. It will therefore use all the tools it can, including emotions, to try to push you to prioritise finding food. Some of the more common emotional hunger signs are:

- feeling irritable or angry;

- increased anxiety;

- being overwhelmed by small things and more stressed than a situation necessitates;

- elevated anxiety around food;

- anxiety at the thought of not having enough to eat, either when you prepare your own food or if others are preparing food for you;

- concerns about being given *too much* food;

- if you are using a meal plan, being resistant to eat above it or even to eat as much as it lays out. This is usually because you know you want to eat several times more than the plan suggests but doing so feels *wrong;*

- an intolerance of empty time in the day or night—having empty time when you are hungry but not letting yourself eat is very difficult to sit with;

- frustration or a sense of despair about your process to overcome the eating disorder or about your future. This can be a sign that you aren't eating enough to meet your high hunger;

- feeling numb and unemotional—an under-resourced body doesn't have energy to waste on emotions, other than anxiety and fear;

- discomfort about spending money on food or spending money generally. This relates to the scarcity mindset that exists due to hunger;

- being overly sensitive to comments about how much you are eating or any weight you have gained because, in truth, you really just want more food;

- irritation or anger towards others who are eating. This can be because you want to be able to eat as freely and feel resentful that they can eat with ease;

- judging others for what or how they are eating, for similar reasons to the above;

- feeling tormented by food;

- eating becoming an overly emotional experience, in positive or negative ways;

- a lack of interest in friends, relationships or things you usually enjoy because you want to be around food and focused solely on that. This typically becomes more prominent when you start to eat more and your brain does all it can to push you to stay at the source of the food and keep eating without distraction.

Behavioural Hunger Signals

Listed below are some behavioural signs of hunger. Everyone is different so consider which of these behaviours you have. Most of the items listed arise from mixed signals in your brain. Part of it is desperate for you to consume more foods and trying to guide you to this but another powerful part still has the addiction to energy deficit and is seeking more of the *hits* that restriction creates. Behavioural hunger signals include:

- calorie counting;

- tracking anything, such as macros, micros, fat grams, carbs etc;

- writing down what you have eaten and keeping food diaries;

- weighing food;

- weighing yourself;

- body checking;

- taking photos of your body;

- taking photos of your food;

- seeking reassurance from others about how much you should eat or around food and your intake in general;

- comparing what you are eating to others;

- seeking out eating disorder recovery blogs, podcasts, videos or accounts for *inspiration* or *motivation*, which really means seeking permission to eat all that you secretly want to;

- binge eating episodes—see Chapter 17 for more on this;

- shopping for food more than necessary, even when you don't buy anything;

- exercising as *permission* to eat more or as a compensatory behaviour;

- purging in other ways, e.g. vomiting, laxatives, diet pills;

- chewing and spitting;

- keeping busy to avoid hunger or eating;

- cooking and baking for others, rarely letting yourself eat it;

- feeding others, getting a sense of reward from watching others eat;

- being fixated with looking at recipes or cookery shows;

- a need to always be in the kitchen or around food, even when you aren't preparing or eating it;

- conversely to the above, avoiding environments where food is present;

- food rituals, strong routines and habits around what you eat, when or how;

- a need for the *perfect* eating situation, such as the right amount of time to eat with no interruptions and everything just as you want it to be before you will eat;

- avoiding social situations or other commitments if they will interrupt your eating routine and becoming anxious if something does. Eating routines are precious to a brain that is energy deprived and so it will drive you to make them a priority;

- checking the time to see if you are *allowed* to eat yet;

- excessive meal planning;

- watching videos or scrolling through accounts of people who are eating to extreme hunger or people undertaking 10,000 calories a day style eating challenges;

- eating slowly, not wanting the eating experience to end or eating very quickly as your body desperately tries to get the food in while it can;

- looking back at food diaries or logs of how much you ate when you were eating more than now;

- delaying eating;

- only allowing yourself to eat as much as or less than another significant person in your life, wishing that they would eat more or eat the foods that you are lusting after;

- avoidance of energy-dense, lower bulk foods because of a fear that they won't fill you up.

These lists are a starting point. They should make you more aware of how much impact being in energy deficit and its inevitable hunger has on you. Recognise all the hunger signals your brain is urgently sending and respond to them. Whenever you notice any of these signs then eat.

And if you do remain in any doubt as to whether you are hungry or not, it's always safer to assume you are!

Chapter 16

Let's Talk About Extreme Hunger

I f I was a betting person, I'd lay bets that this chapter of the book is one of the most popular. This is because:

1. You are in energy deficit and your body is semi-starved, so the hunger signalling side of your brain is doing all it can to let you know how hungry you are. But in another part of your brain, you have a powerful addiction to energy deficit which gives rise to agitation, anxiety and distress if you do decide to eat to meet the hunger. This results in on-going inner conflict, leaving you feeling confused and overwhelmed. You just want someone to take it all away and tell you that eating is the right thing to do because you are so hungry.

2. Effectively, you are seeking permission to eat more because doing so feels so wrong but also very right.

3. Your mental hunger is constant and no amount of food seems to ever be enough. You are naturally seeking reassurance that it is ok to keep responding to your hunger in the quantities you are and with food types that you might have labelled as *unhealthy* or *bad*.

4. You have been told by other people, whether that's a partner, family, friends or a *professional* that you are binging and need to eat less but you don't believe their advice is correct (it isn't).

5. No one around you has ever experienced hunger like this or eats the high amounts you are capable of at the moment or would be capable of if you allowed yourself to give into it, so you want to feel less alone.

In simple terms, when you come back to this section of the book, it's because your hunger and drive to eat is extremely high but you aren't letting yourself respond or judging your hunger. You are seeking permission, inspiration or reassurance. If this is you then please, put the book down and go grab a pizza, some creamy coleslaw and warm-baked cookies to munch on as a snack while you continue to read.

The phenomenon of extreme hunger is unique to people emerging from a state of energy deficit. In the Western world, this most commonly occurs in people who are overcoming restrictive eating disorders and so it's a largely unknown concept to the public or even to health professionals. This makes it a frightening and lonely experience.

Addicted to Energy Deficit provides detailed information about the concept of *hyperphagia*, which is the medical term for the drive to eat a lot of food (extreme hunger). It explains the causes of the high levels of hunger experienced by people in a semi-starved and energy deficit state. There's also an exploration of the research that demonstrates that the drive to eat amounts that can exceed 10,000 calories a day is a normal physiological response to insufficient stored energy supplies.

The key points to take from *Addicted to Energy Deficit* to aid your understanding in this chapter are:

1. The drive to eat huge amounts of food when your body doesn't have enough stored energy is normal. It's a survival response which shouldn't be ignored.

2. The excessive hunger experienced can take you to very high intakes which someone who isn't in energy deficit wouldn't be able to eat but it's normal for your current situation.

3. Episodes of extreme hunger coincide with fat and lean tissue stores that remain below your set point. As fat restores faster than lean tissue, a degree of fat overshoot is needed to gain all the necessary lean tissue stores. Until this happens, your hunger will remain high.

4. When your body has fully restored and is comfortable at your set point, confident that another famine is not around the corner, your hunger will normalise to that of an average Joe. This means that your urges to eat everything and more won't last forever if you go the full course and keep aiming for overshoot to fully repair, while simultaneously reprogramming your brain.

The Emotional Response to Extreme Hunger

You are likely to experience a range of emotions when extreme hunger kicks in. If you are at the stage of contemplating change or beginning to make small changes, with an ongoing powerful drive to restrict, then having very high hunger can increase your anxiety and distress. You want to eat and it's so hard to keep denying yourself the food that your brain and body are demanding but the ability to finally abstain from the restriction that has long been your automatic stress response still feels out of reach.

When you do let go and respond to extreme hunger, it can be exhilarating and empowering to have this drive to eat that you are now capable of responding to, eating all the foods the eating disorder kept off limits for so long. However, after a while, you might find that it becomes harder to keep responding to it. Eating as much food as extreme hunger demands is a time-consuming process. It also requires ongoing mental energy and focus to keep responding to your hunger and continue to go against the lingering restrictive habits that remain automatic if you aren't vigilant. This means that other things in your life can be difficult to keep up with when you are going through extreme hunger. You know that to successfully overcome the eating disorder, you need to keep responding to it, which often means that you have to put other things on the back-burner for a while. Some people go through periods in which they want to withdraw from the world to eat all that their body is demanding and you might also experience episodes of frustration, feeling like it will never end.

When you feel physically full and uncomfortable but still have a deep drive to eat, you will feel torn and confused about what to respond to. Should it be your body saying, *I'm full,* or your brain saying, *I'm still hungry?* You know rationally that it's right to respond to the deep drive to eat but doing so can feel wrong and create feelings of guilt and greed.

Once you have gained some weight but the drive to eat remains high, you will have times when you just want it all to be over, believing that your body shouldn't *need* this much food any longer, with thoughts that surely you can't still be in energy deficit. This can be another confusing and anxiety-provoking time. You will face internal battles over whether to keep responding to your deep hunger or listen to the persuasive thoughts that you should, *Try to eat normal amounts now.*

Another confusing situation is when people around you comment on how much you are eating and you are constantly eating several times more than others, when not so long ago you were the one eating the least. This can reinforce the belief that you are doing the wrong thing. In these moments, you will need even more willpower, strength and determination to keep focused on what's right for you and stay on the path you set out on.

And because you do still have a restrictive eating disorder, even though you are doing all you can to overcome it, the predictably boring but still very powerful emotional reactions to eating more food will also be present. I'm talking about the feelings of guilt, greed, shame and regret; the anxiety response both as you eat more and afterwards; the fear-based thoughts that eating all this food will lead you to gain weight too fast or that your weight gain will never stop and the deep-seated discomforting feeling of wrong-doing that you can't quite rationalise but feels real.

At times you will find yourself in a no man's land of feeling helpless because you don't think that you can keep going forwards but you don't know that you can or want to go back either.

Perhaps most of all, you will feel exhausted and drained in ways you are not used to when the eating disorder was still giving you that false energy high created by the migratory response.

Overall, when it comes to your emotional reactions to extreme hunger, seek out positivity and enjoyment from it whenever you can. Choose to be excited by it. When it gets boring and exhausting eating all this food every single waking hour, give things a shake-up. Seek out new foods and new eating opportunities, find ways to go a bit more wild and free and bring the interest and excitement back to the process. You have lived in a numb, dull and uptight eating disordered world for too long. This is your time to enjoy life, food and not being hungry so embrace it. When the feelings of greed and regret and thoughts to put the brakes on your eating set in, just flick them away and keep munching happily. You deserve to.

How Do You Cope With Extreme Hunger?

When you understand what extreme hunger is and the physiology behind it, you can feel reassured that this drive to eat that feels insatiable and out of control is just a normal body and brain trying to restore and survive. Learn about it and understand it so that when it's there you can rationalise why you are experiencing it and feel less anxious about responding (well perhaps a bit less anxious anyway!). Reassure yourself that high hunger in anyone in a state of energy deficit is normal.

Once you have educated yourself about extreme hunger, also educate those around you, such as the people you live or spend time with. When they can understand why you are suddenly eating so much more than you ever used to and the part it plays in your process to find freedom from the eating disorder, they can support you through it.

Remember that a brain screaming for food despite a full belly is a normal part of this process. It's distressing but you aren't broken. Your brain is the intellect and that's the part to listen and respond to. Your stomach just needs to catch up but it will if you keep eating.

Of course, eating high amounts, especially if you are eating foods your body is craving which are likely to be of higher density, will lead to weight gain. However, weight gain needs to happen to overcome the eating disorder and responding to extreme hunger is more likely to positively reprogram your brain. This is because, by responding to extreme hunger, you will fully abstain from restriction which is what's needed. Not responding to all your hunger is to continue to restrict, even if you are eating more than you were before. The weight gain needs to happen, so you might as well let your body restore and your brain reprogram most effectively.

At times, eating to extreme hunger will be exhausting. When your body final-ly gets the energy that it has been seeking, the evolutionary migratory response triggered by energy deficit will switch off. When this happens, your high energy levels and need to keep moving your body will reduce and exhaustion can hit and it can hit hard. Your brain now recognises that you don't need to migrate to find food as you have foods available, so you can finally stop, rest and eat. Now your brain will do all it can to preserve the energy supplies you have and build more. To do this, it will keep sending the high hunger signals while also sending signals of exhaustion so it can use the energy that's now coming in to do essential repair works, restore organs and tissues and slowly begin to switch back on non-essential functions that it turned off to preserve precious resources while you were in starvation mode. Listen to the hunger and listen to the exhaustion. Respond to both. Eat, rest and sleep.

You are also likely to experience food cravings at times, perhaps even for weird and wonderful combinations. Go with it. Your body asks for the foods it needs when it needs them, depending on what repair work it's doing at that particular time. There will be times you will want more sugary foods, sometimes it will be dairy products or proteins and other times more carbohydrates or lots of fats. One thing is guaranteed, your body will consistently drive you towards higher-density foods because it needs all the energy it can get at the moment. If you try to convince yourself you are craving lettuce while you are emerging from energy deficit, then question it! Overall, follow what your brain is guiding you towards when it comes to food choices while also consistently eating new and varied foods, so your brain recognises that all the food types it needs are now available.

When hunger is at its highest, it's likely to be there day and night. If you wake up in the night hungry and thinking of food, you need to respond and eat. Keep food by your bed so you can grab it without having to get up. For humans, sleep is as critical as food and your brain will protect its ability to get sufficient sleep because it's so essential to brain function and life. When your brain goes to the lengths of pushing you to eat at night, it means it's decided that getting that extra energy in trumps the need for precious sleep. You need to respect this and respond.

The next point is that extreme hunger is different for everyone. It goes to different extremes for everyone. You will hear some people say they ate 10,000 calories a day, some 6,000 and others say 15,000. Some will say they ate McDonald's every day for weeks and others ate whole cakes or jars of Nutella. For some people, it lasts a few weeks and others months or even a year or more. Don't try to compare to anyone else or do what they did. Every single body is different and what yours asks for will not be the same as someone else and that's as it should be. To overcome the eating disorder, you need to learn to tune into what your body asks you for and respond. You can't do that if you are trying to eat in the same way as some random person you found on social media. Your body is unique so embrace it, trusting that your experiences with extreme hunger and in overcoming the eating disorder are right for you.

And just in case anyone needs a reminder. Extreme hunger can happen at any weight or BMI. It doesn't matter if you are starting from a point of a *normal*, *overweight* or *obese* body type. If you are overcoming a restrictive eating disorder and have high hunger then you respond to it, just as much as the next person. Refer back to Chapter Six about the additional challenges of being in a bigger body with a restrictive eating disorder.

Will it Last Forever?

Extreme hunger won't last forever, especially if you honour it. For some it lasts a few months, for others, it can last a year or more, but when your body is ready, your hunger will normalise.

And when your high hunger subsides, you will continue to eat without any level of restriction, you just won't feel the desire to eat extreme amounts. Rest assured though that this doesn't mean you go back to feeling as if you are depriving yourself of the foods you want. If you do feel like this is the case then you are still restricting and your hunger is higher than you are admitting.

Extreme Hunger is a Golden Ticket

I always say that extreme hunger can be your golden ticket to an eating disorder-free life if you are brave and respond to it.

This is when you learn what food your body needs and to give it those foods. You also begin to understand that no amount of food or food type is to be feared and you begin to live more authentically and proudly than ever before.

To Conclude

When you experience extreme hunger, keep going. Your body and brain have your survival as their top priority so listen and respond to the messages to eat and rest. Even when it's an emotional rollercoaster and you don't think you can or should continue, just keep going. It won't last forever. Keep aiming for overshoot and the extreme hunger will eventually settle down to a hunger that is still high but not insanely so. Your body knows what it needs to do so trust it.

Chapter 17

Don't Fight the Binges

H aving read the last chapter about extreme hunger and the level of eating it can drive you to, some of you might now have thoughts that extreme hunger is a description of binge eating and someone who is out of control. You might even consider it as someone who has flipped from a restrictive eating disorder to a binge eating disorder and is ultimately no better off.

If these are your thoughts then please read back over the last chapter about why extreme hunger occurs and the reasons your body needs this much food. If you want even more of the science to the concept of hyperphagia then refer to the information I included in *Addicted to Energy Deficit*. Extreme hunger is a normal physiological response to a body in energy deficit.

But it might help to also understand what true binge eating is.

What is Considered Binge Eating?

People with restrictive eating disorders can experience episodes of true binge eating. This is not binge eating disorder. For a diagnosis of binge eating disorder, you need to have regular episodes of binge eating <u>without</u> any kind of restrictive eating or compensatory behaviours around the binge eating episodes. If you binge as part of a restrictive eating disorder, you are very likely to be in a binge-restrict cycle. This is when a binging episode is followed by restrictive eating and/or purging, exercising or another form of compensatory behaviour in an attempt to *undo* it. The binge eating episodes are caused by your current state of energy deficit. The restriction or compensation following a binge maintains the energy deficit and this drives the next binge in the cycle. In this way, restriction and energy deficit cause the binges.

Binge eating within a restrictive eating disorder is your brain doing all it can to get sufficient energy. To break the binge-restrict cycle you need to address the restriction and compensatory behaviours by abstaining from these, while still allowing the binges to happen when they do. Once you are out of energy deficit and your brain trusts that food is going to continue to come in without needing to drive a binge for it, the binges will stop naturally. It takes courage and determination not to purge after a binge and to get up the next morning and reach for a huge breakfast while resting on the couch. But the more you do just that, the sooner you will be able to eat freely to your hunger, without binge eating episodes and the challenges they bring.

What is the Difference Between Binge Eating and Extreme Hunger?

The physiological explanation for both binge eating and eating to meet extreme hunger is the same. Your body is in energy deficit and your brain needs all the energy that it can get to restore energy balance. Some people's brains will drive them to binge eat to address this, in addition to the extreme hunger that becomes increasingly difficult to resist—something common to nearly everyone when they start to eat with less restriction.

There are some key differences between binge eating and eating to extreme hunger. Understanding these will allow you to know if you are experiencing true binges or merely responding to your high hunger levels.

The first thing to make clear is that both extreme hunger and binge eating are normal and biologically driven when semi-starved. There's nothing to be ashamed of about either. Both will resolve as you overcome the eating disorder and emerge from energy deficit.

In terms of differences between binge and extreme hunger eating, binge eating is defined as, *eating within a 2-hour window an amount of food, larger than most people would eat in a similar period of time, with an accompanying feeling of loss of control over what or how much you are eating*[1]. On the other hand, with eating to extreme hunger, although you can eat similar amounts in short periods, you remain in control of what you are doing. You are consciously choosing your foods and you could make yourself stop if you had to.

A good analogy for binge eating is that it's similar to if you have held your breath for too long. Sooner or later, even if you try to keep holding your breath, your body and brain will take over and you will inhale a huge intake of air in one go, followed by more deep breaths to get the oxygen. The same with binge eating. Your brain has decided to take over because it can't tolerate the energy deprivation any longer and so it forces you to *inhale* or consume a huge amount of food very quickly.

With extreme hunger, on the other hand, we might use the analogy of not having had enough to drink over the past 24 hours, leaving you slightly dehydrated and thirsty. Your thoughts keep returning to water as your brain is attempting to push you to drink and you find it hard to focus on anything else. When water is available, you will want to drink several glasses to rehydrate your body and that water will feel and taste amazing. However, you can still resist the water if you have to. This is the same with extreme hunger. Unlike a binge, you can stop yourself eating if you choose to, even though it can get harder to stop once you start to respond.

In addition to the sense of loss of control that accompanies binge eating, binge episodes can become ritualised and you might find that you start to plan for them and even look forward to them. Rituals can develop with where you binge, what time you will give into the urges and what foods you will have available. These rituals can make the binge episodes feel comforting and safe. When it comes to eating to extreme hunger, some patterns and rituals can develop but as extreme hunger often kicks in just as you are breaking your restrictive eating habits and the rituals you had around those, it's less likely you will have rituals with extreme hunger.

Another difference between binge eating and extreme hunger is that binge eating is very commonly associated with feelings of shame and guilt and binges are often carried out in secret. Eating to extreme hunger can be accompanied by similar feelings and a sense of not wanting to be seen eating but it can equally come with excitement and joy at finally being able to eat freely and even a justified sense of pride to the point that you actually want the world to see.

How Much Food is Considered a Binge or Extreme Hunger?

There's no clear answer to this. Definitions of binge eating don't give figures or amounts but just specify that it's a *large* amount in a short period. To be clear though, a large amount is generally considered to be thousands of calories in that 1-2 hour period, not just a couple of bowls of cereal. Extreme hunger can also drive you to consume similar amounts but it's important not to get too hung up on amounts or numbers. Eat what your body needs and trust it to know what it's doing.

As a result of the amount of food that both binge eating and extreme hunger can lead to, both eating types can create physical, mental and emotional distress. These feelings and emotions are part of the process and if you keep going despite them, it will get easier. Don't allow difficult feelings and emotions to be a reason to go back to restriction and eating disordered habits. The now appeal (covered in *Addicted to Energy Deficit*) is a real risk that keeps people trapped inside an eating disorder or addiction. This is where you seek that momentary fix to feel better in the now but it leads to longer-term misery. Keep your focus on the future, dealing with the distress now for the ultimate freedom that you deserve.

Overall, don't fight the binges or the high levels of eating that extreme hunger can lead to. Both of these responses are a result of your brain seeking extraordinary ways to deal with a critical situation, which is the energy deficit, semi-starved state you are in. Trust your brain and body to do what they need to. They need you to get extreme amounts of energy on board at the moment. Eat to all your hunger and if binges happen then let them, no matter how much food that drives you to. Keep determined; stay on course and it will settle down over time as you emerge from energy deficit and reach energy balance.

1. American Psychiatric Association. Diagnostic and statistical manual of mental disorders. 2022 (5th ed., text rev.). https://doi.org/10.1176/appi.books.9780890425787.

Chapter 18

Aim to Eat Mindlessly

When someone overcoming an eating disorder tells me they are now aiming to eat mindfully, my heart sinks. As much as I appreciate all the benefits of mindfulness and meditation, mindful eating is not advantageous to someone trying to overcome a restrictive eating disorder.

Mindful eating is defined as, *In the moment awareness of the food and drink you put into your body.* It's something that diet culture promotes in the name of *health.* When you have a restrictive eating disorder, one of your superpowers is very likely to be using your mind when it comes to eating. Your mind is hyper-aware of most morsels of food you put into your body, with a vigilance that's rarely proven beneficial.

You are likely excellent at mindfully calculating what to eat, when, how much, who with and where and that these thoughts consume you in exhausting and distressing ways. Therefore, eating *mindfully* is a terrible idea when you have an eating disorder because it exacerbates your belief that you need to control your eating and that you can't trust your body to guide you in the right direction. I'm sure mindful eating advocates will argue that mindful eating is about being in tune with your body. However, if you have to sit and rate your hunger before your next mouthful or eat slowly to savour everything about the food you are eating, then I think you will find that you've engaged in more restrictive eating methods that your addicted brain will hotly pursue.

Practising mindful eating is a big risk. It can lead to a prolonged struggle to fully break free of the eating disorder and to the development of more disordered behaviours that remove the pleasure from being able to eat freely and happily.

The best approach to your eating now and for your future is to do the very thing that we were born to do...

Eat mindLESSly!

Children and animals do not eat mindfully. Their bodies guide them as to what they need to eat and how much. A child who has not yet been influenced by diet culture and the sugar police, left to choose what they want to eat when they want it, will naturally choose foods that overall provide a range of nutrients and all the food groups. Foods that are appropriate for their age and stage of development. They don't only choose to eat sweets and there's nothing mindful in their food selection. It's only when adults interfere and tell children what they *should* and *shouldn't* eat that the problems start.

So, rather than aiming for mindful eating, shoot for mindless eating. Aim to eat without thought, calculation or manipulation, not needing to remember what you ate earlier or consider what you will eat later. Eat because you are hungry or you want to. If food's available and you want to eat it, then do so, without any more thought. Using your mind is when the problems start.

If you get an urge to eat chocolate cookies or a big plate of pasta then do it. Don't waste time questioning it or mentally negotiating.

When you can learn how to eat mindlessly, without any thought processing beyond a quick decision on the what (based on genuine desire), pushing all mental gymnastics to one side and when you can learn to eat in the way you would have done before the eating disorder started and as children do; then you will truly let the eating disorder go and find mental space to focus on the far more important things in your life.

So, to get started, aim to mindfully eat mindlessly. In doing so, you will soon discover the healthy freedom of being able to mindlessly eat mindlessly!

Chapter 19

An Introduction to Compensatory Behaviours

C ompensatory behaviours refer to anything that you engage in as a way to compensate for the foods you have eaten. Your brain will seek its drug, which is energy deficit, by driving you towards restrictive eating and any number of compensatory behaviours. When you first engaged in a behaviour or restrictive form of eating that resulted in a deeper energy deficit, your brain noticed what created this high reward response so that it could push you to repeat it. In this way, these behaviours quickly became compulsive and hard to stop.

Everyone with a restrictive eating disorder has a different *cocktail* of restrictive eating and compensatory behavioural habits that make up the eating disorder. Some engage in a greater level of restrictive eating but with less compensatory behaviours, while others might continue to eat more freely but engage in very compulsive behaviours to compensate. The majority of people have a balance of both restriction and compensatory behaviours.

For many, the balance of restriction and compensatory behaviours shifts over time or the behaviours change. This can be because the degree of energy deficit you have been engaging in is no longer providing sufficient reward to your brain and so you need a deeper level to get the same hit. This is comparable to other addictions, where, over time, more of the drug is needed to get the same effects. The other reason behaviours or restrictive eating patterns can shift is that your circumstances change. Perhaps you take a more sedentary job and you can no longer engage in the movement you were doing and so you adopt other behaviours to compensate or your level of restrictive eating increases to achieve the same degree of energy deficit. Or maybe your living situation changes and more people in your home environment make it harder to purge through vomiting without anyone knowing so you switch to another form of compensation.

No matter what your behaviours and level of restriction are, it's all powerfully addictive and all needs to be addressed to fully overcome the eating disorder.

As explained previously, abstaining from everything at once is often the most effective and easiest option to overcome an eating disorder. Addressing everything together helps you to avoid the risk of tackling one behaviour only to find that another one sneaks in or increases, whereby your brain has just found an alternative route to the same hit of energy deficit.

When you reflect on your unique cocktail of eating disorder behaviours and restrictive eating patterns, identify everything and ideally decide to address it all together. But if you do choose to moderate one behaviour and focus on stopping another, be very self-aware and mindful that the other behaviours don't creep up in their intensity or the amount of time you spend engaging in them. Eating disorders can be sneaky and insidious—keep reflecting on where it's showing up and find ways to address it.

The following chapters cover some of the most common compensatory behaviours in more detail, including how to address and ideally abstain from them.

Not every possible compensatory behaviour is covered, so forgive me for that. However, a lot of the information is transferable to other behaviours so use it for whatever your patterns of compensatory behaviour happen to be. It all matters.

Chapter 20

Compulsive Exercise & Movement

C ompulsive movement or exercise is a key part of an eating disorder for the vast majority of people and living with it is miserable. A very high number of people with restrictive eating disorders are affected by some level of compulsive movement. This is because movement compulsions arise from two powerful sources—a brain seeking any means to achieve energy deficit and the migratory response.

The migratory response stems from the evolutionary explanation that restrictive eating disorders were a key survival mechanism in our hunter/gatherer ancestors. An energy deficit would signal to their brain that they were in a scarce environment and so there was a need to keep moving (migrate) to find a new dense foraging ground. The drive to keep moving kept our ancestors alive but today it carries the opposite risk.

Feeling compelled to keep moving your body, with powerful feelings of wrongdoing or agitation if you don't, makes this component of a restrictive eating disorder a strong maintaining factor because it can be incredibly hard to break.

There were times when I didn't think I'd ever be able to overcome the compulsive exercise and movement habits because of how powerful they were. Even when I managed to eat more and gain some weight during spells in treatment or early *recovery attempts*, my exercise compulsions only strengthened.

Happily, I can report that even a strongly embedded movement or exercise compulsion can be overcome. A fact that's now been verified by many clients I've worked with. However, it does take perseverance, eating a lot of food and sitting or sobbing through moments of high agitation, anxiety, brain fog and despair, as well as feelings of guilt and grief. A brain with such a strong addiction will try everything to push you back to the behaviours that lead to the fix it's desperate for. This means that when you do abstain, as with any addiction, you experience a period of dopamine deficit which creates all the common symptoms of withdrawal which are very uncomfortable to sit with.

However, the symptoms will slowly subside if you can keep going despite the challenging withdrawal symptoms and overwhelming urges to move and exercise, resisting your habitual walking, running or lower-level movement patterns. Your brain will reprogram. Brain circuits driving old habits will begin to *unwire*, while your desired new habits will *wire in* with ongoing repetition. And when you emerge from energy deficit, the migratory response will also switch off.

Achieving this might be one of the hardest things you ever go through but you can get through it and finally be free of any exercise or movement compulsions you have, no matter how entrenched and long-standing they are.

Remain mindful that to overcome compulsive movement, your brain will use every trick in the book to try to deter you. One of the most common patterns it uses to entice you into movement when you attempt to abstain is to generate credible thoughts that the movement or exercise you are choosing to engage in is because it's *normal*, you need *fresh air* or *that it's good for anxiety*. Therefore, you will become convinced that the walk you are taking is nothing to do with the eating disorder's addictive drive.

When you are first overcoming the eating disorder, engaging in any unnecessary exercise, walks or movement is not a good idea. No matter how much you try to persuade yourself that it's innocent and won't hurt, it very likely isn't innocent and it will fire up the movement pathways in your brain's eating disorder network, which in turn will create stronger urges to restrict or trigger negative body image thoughts. To overcome the addictive nature of movement and your brain using it to pursue the addictive *hit* from energy deficit, you need to stop as much as possible. This will increase the likelihood that your body fully emerges from energy deficit and that your brain reprograms.

But let's say that you are now at a point at which your body has been fully restored. You have gained a good amount of weight because you have been abstaining well from all your restrictive eating habits and compensatory behaviours, including movement. Your body size and shape seem to have settled and you feel physically that things are healing. At what point can you consider it to be safe to return to more movement? How do you know if the thoughts that you would like to go on a walk today because the weather is great are still coming from the eating disorder or if this desire is now free of any eating disorder-generated compulsion? You have done all this hard work to get where you are and don't want to risk reigniting old addictive habits and brain pathways but when is it safe?

This was a question that I had to do some deep reflective work on for myself. Was the walk to the shops or the lower level movement I was engaging in, especially now I was a stable and *healthy* weight, still compulsive or at risk of becoming so?

To answer this, I came up with some pointers of when movement or exercise was still compulsive and to be avoided and what would indicate that it's safe to engage in a bit more again. I recommend clients use these indicators as a starting point to making this judgement call, with the caveat that full honesty is needed when reflecting on them.

Indicators to Help Determine if Exercise or Movement is Compulsive:

- You experience guilt when you are not exercising or moving.

- Agitation or anxiety escalates if you are not able to exercise, stand or move.

- An association lingers in your brain between movement and how much you eat or the food types you consume.

- Movement is motivated by any form of body shape and weight manipulation, even if that's strength training or bodybuilding and not weight loss.

- When you ask the question, *If it was guaranteed that I wouldn't gain weight if I didn't exercise or move now, would I do it?* and if you are honest with yourself, you wouldn't.

- Your urges to exercise or to move interfere with your ability to socialise, have normal relationships, or have a job, hobbies or travel that involve being sedentary.

- There is rigidity or obsession over the what, when and how much you engage in. This might be an obsession over steps, distances or laps; it might involve logging movement in some way; having rules about when in the day or week you have to exercise or set times you are *allowed* to sit down.

- You cannot stop the exercise even when sick or injured. Exercising with flu or an injury is not normal, healthy or fun!

- People comment on how much exercise you do, which might also make you feel good and give you a sense of martyrdom.

- The urge to move occupies your thoughts and distracts you from conversations, work, reading or other things because you are consumed by thoughts of when you can exercise or move next, even feeling anxious and agitated about it.

- At times, you don't want to move or exercise but you feel that you have to and can't stop yourself from pulling on your shoes even though doing so is making you miserable.

- You will take any opportunity to move your body in any small way possible. For example, standing or sitting but swinging your foot or leg, twitching muscles or clenching. You find it very hard to just be still.

- You can't sit comfortably and relax if you think there is washing up to be done, housework or laundry to do, a pet to feed or anything else that means you can get up and move.

When some or all of the above points still apply, even if only in a very small way, the movement is still compulsive and the way to address it is to stop it until you are 110% sure that none of these markers of ongoing exercise compulsion feature at all. As you are overcoming the compulsion, you will find that these indicators apply less and therefore might convince yourself that you are ok now. For example, you might be very happy to now sit and relax or be sedentary at work and in the evenings all week, with no agitation or anxiety, but on a

Saturday afternoon, trying to sit and watch a film still creates uncomfortable feelings. This shows the compulsion is still there, even if you are much better than you once were—it just needs a little longer to fully rewire your brain pathways.

A fixation on movement to the point that it interferes with the rest of your life is not normal and it's disabling. But most of all, it's miserable.

Abstaining from exercise and movement and finding ways to stop yourself from engaging will be an up-and-down process. Some battles you will win and some you will lose, but each time you don't put on those shoes and head out the door or sit eating cookies instead of standing and pacing, you will be taking important steps towards essential brain reprogramming.

It's also important to remind you that it doesn't matter what weight you are in this process at the start, middle or end. Even if you are already in the overweight or obese weight range by BMI as you begin to overcome exercise compulsions and the eating disorder, you still need to stop and rest as much as someone who is in that *underweight* range. The size of your body doesn't tell you about the internal damage you might have as a result of the eating disorder or that your body still needs time, rest and nourishment to heal. And the brain reprogramming required is also just as critical.

When you are fully out of energy deficit, have reached a stable weight that you are very confident is your set weight, your overshoot has settled and you have allowed a good amount of time for the brain reprogramming to fully embed, then return to the indicators above. If you can put your hand on your heart and say none of the points above apply in any way, no matter how small, you are possibly ready to experiment with having a normal and more healthy relationship with movement again—if that is what you want.

For some, exercise and movement is not something they have a lot of pull towards once they have fully overcome the eating disorder and that's absolutely fine. You can have a very happy and healthy future life without exercise featuring. For those who do decide to re-engage, take it slow, be very self-aware and avoid forms of movement and exercise that are based on aesthetics or on a need to be lighter such as bodybuilding, ballet, gymnastics or running.

Chapter 21

Why All Levels of Exercise & Lower-Level Movement Matter

The exercise and lower-level movement components of a restrictive eating disorder can manifest in different ways, each of which can be equally compulsive and addictive. Being aware of it and why it is important to address everything, no matter how small or innocent it seems, will help you to overcome it.

Formal forms of exercise are easier to identify. Putting your trainers on, going for a run, swimming, the gym and formal sports are blatant forms of *exercise*. Most people understand that they need to stop these, even if they don't like the idea.

What about lighter exercise though? The, *Well it's good for me and my doctor even says it's ok,* forms of movement. Walking, yoga or pilates are often recommended as being not only good for our bodies but great for our mental health.

Indeed, these things can be great for the mental health of someone without an addiction to energy deficit and compulsive movement. But the impact that any exercise has on the mental health of someone with an addiction to it will be detrimental and worsen over time. *Addicted to Energy Deficit* explains the neuroscience in more detail but essentially any calming effects you perceive to get from exercise are coming from the *fix* that the movement gives you, in the same way as any addictive drug or behaviour. With every *fix* you gain, you simultaneously create a deeper overall dopamine deficit which results in depression, anxiety and agitation whenever you are not engaging in the addiction. Over time, you therefore need more of your *drug* (in this case exercise) for the same level of calming effect.

In short then, not only does compulsive exercise not have mental health benefits, it actually leads to a longer term decline in your mental health.

I can also report first-hand that swapping a more intense form of exercise for something *lighter* doesn't work. In *treatment*, I was encouraged to stop exercising but told I could carry on with some walking, encouraged to try yoga, and advised to swap the gym for swimming. These trade-ins only made me more addicted and maintained or deepened the energy deficit state I was in. Making these trade-ins simply switched how I got the *fix* my brain was seeking from one method to another.

And in doing so, I became filled with dread at not taking my habitual walk at noon, I couldn't go a day without doing yoga and swimming became faster and with more lengths. If anything interrupted or if I tried to take a break from it, my levels of anxiety and agitation peaked. Life is miserable when you can't see a friend because you have to fit in a yoga session or you push yourself to go for a walk despite having flu.

Therefore, all forms of exercise, whether it's intensive running or swimming or it's walking or yoga, need to be addressed and stopped.

But let's also consider the lower-level forms of movement.

Lower-level movement is a term used to describe all the forms of movement a person engages in throughout the day just to go about their daily tasks. Examples might be walking about the house as you go from room to room, standing at work because you work in a shop and need to assist customers or getting the family dinner ready. Most people engage in lower-level movement every day without giving it a second thought, considering it as a form of exercise or relating it to their food intake. But with restrictive eating disorders, lower-level movement can be another form of compensatory behaviour that becomes incredibly compulsive. You will be very aware of just how much you engage in. Or perhaps, that should be that you will be very aware of just how much you *don't* engage in because it's then that your anxiety and agitation escalate.

Lower-level movement is something that's often overlooked in the process of *treating* eating disorders because the food or more intense forms of exercise become the main focus. Unfortunately, failing to address the lower-level movement will only exacerbate how hard it is to also overcome everything else.

Some examples of compulsive lower-level movement are given below. Use these to help you reflect on and recognise your habits:

- standing when you could be sitting.

- housework

- gardening

- using the upstairs loo when there's one downstairs

- taking stairs rather than the lift

- deliberately parking the car further away from the store for the extra few metres you will then need to walk

- visiting every aisle of the supermarket when all you went in for was a loaf of bread

- standing on public transport even when there are plenty of seats

- jiggling your leg when sitting

- vacuuming when it doesn't need to be done

- taking the rubbish out in small amounts, rather than all in one go

- doing the laundry and putting it away one piece at a time rather than all at once

- insisting on doing the washing up and getting irritated if anyone else tries to do it.

Any small level of movement you engage in because sitting and being still feels too hard can be considered compulsive lower-level movement. However, sitting and being still is a skill you need to develop and when you do, you will be so relieved that you did.

Chapter 22

Stopping Compulsive Movement: Rest & Relaxation

The ability to rest and relax your body and mind is an important life skill. It's also something that the combination of compulsive movement and an overly alert and busy brain, two things common to people with restrictive eating disorders, will rob you of.

Learning the skill of rest and relaxation will make a significant difference as you are overcoming the eating disorder and abstaining from the associated behaviours, including exercise and movement. But learning any new skill is hard—even more so when the skill you want to develop pulls you away from habits with strong addictive qualities. But just because something is hard, doesn't mean you can't push through with determination. If you are going to abstain from exercise and lower-level movement then you might as well put the extra time doing so gives you to good use—rest and relax, while eating lots of delicious food.

Of course, I appreciate that it's not as easy as, *Just do it!*

Therefore, some tools are provided below to help you to develop the skill of rest and relaxation. Nothing will completely remove the emotions, anxiety and agitation that you might get or the amount of mental focus you will need. However, these tools can help to keep you on course, enabling you to continue to rest, despite powerful urges to move.

Tools to Help You Rest and Relax

1. Eating enough food... where *enough* means A LOT

Conversely to what you might believe, eating a lot more food can make all the difference to your movement compulsions. Abstaining from restriction and other behaviours at the same time as resting your body will pull your brain out of the eating disorder neural networks, making you less compelled to follow any of your old habits. The fact you are eating a lot and being still will also demonstrate to your brain that you are safe and have a good supply of food in your environment. It will therefore be more likely to switch off the urges to keep moving generated by the migratory response. When your brain does turn the migratory response off, you are also likely to feel higher levels of exhaustion than you have for a long time and this is when hunger can escalate. Notice these signals, respect them and respond.

Even if you believe that eating a lot more will only increase your urges to exercise to compensate, do it anyway. Eat large amounts. Implement the tips below to keep as sedentary as possible and with enough consistency, the urges and compulsions to keep moving will subside.

2. Make a sedentary plan

In the early days of pushing yourself to rest more, it can help to create a plan of sedentary distractions to engage in during the times of day that you are usually most active. Be specific with this at first.

Write out what you will do and when so it keeps you more accountable and you aren't trying to make decisions in moments when your anxiety is at a peak. This way you know, for example, that at 11 am you will sit down to phone your mum with snacks in your hand and at 3 pm you will be watching the next episode of Gilmore Girls on Netflix with a tub of ice cream. I choose Gilmore Girls as that's what I watched during this time but you can pick something that suits your tastes which are almost certainly more sophisticated than mine!

An important point to note: all sedentary activities planned should be food inclusive. This is not the time to deploy old tactics of keeping busy to avoid eating.

3. Be accountable

Indeed you do ultimately need to be accountable to yourself but this might not be enough at first because your brain has a powerful addiction that is very persuasive at allowing you to believe that going on long walks or doing some vacuuming is ok. External validation that those thoughts are untrue can make the difference between whether you succeed at resting or give in to the compulsions.

Find someone to be accountable to, whether that's a family member, friend, coach or other professional. Appoint someone to be honest with about your engagement in movement or exercise. This can be a key reminder to you as to why you are doing this and ensure it remains a priority when other things try to take over.

4. The feet off the floor challenge

This is a great game to play.

The object of the game is to keep your feet off the floor for as much of the day as you possibly can. The only times your feet can touch the ground are when you are walking to the kitchen to get food and back to the couch or your bed with food. Trips to the bathroom are also allowed, as long as you are only going when you really need to go and not just as an excuse to get up and move about.

Making it a game can bring in an element of fun and playfulness which can also help reduce anxiety. Of course, it should go without saying, that while sitting or lying without your feet on the floor, there shouldn't be any other sneaky forms of exercise or movement happening.

5. Physiological sighs for anxiety

We've all heard the advice to take deep breaths if someone is feeling anxious. However, physiological sighs are a breathing technique that neuroscientists now recommend as one of the quickest ways to bring your body out of a stress response. They can be helpful when you are aiming to rest and relax but doing so is causing your anxiety to rise.

Physiological sighs are two quick inhalations through the nose followed by a slower exhalation through the mouth. This is covered in more detail in Chapter 53.

6. Respond to all your hunger

This tip is similar to the first one (eat!) but for a different reason.

Movement, exercise and keeping busy have become your learnt response to block hunger signals. This made restricting your food intake easier to tolerate. When you begin to rest, allowing your adrenaline and cortisol levels which usually blunt your hunger to reduce, you are likely to feel more of the true hunger that was always there. When this happens, you should respond and eat, no matter how much food it takes to satiate your hunger. Sitting and resting is torturous when you are hungry and not letting yourself eat, so eating to match your hunger will make the process a lot less miserable. The other benefit is that when you eat without restriction and rest, you are unwiring the links in your brain between food and movement and wiring in new learning that how much you eat and how much you move are not related.

7. Reassure yourself

It's great to have someone else to reassure you when you are anxious and doing something hard, but sometimes there isn't anyone available for this when you need them and you only have yourself.

Tell yourself that you are doing the right thing by resting, even if you don't believe it at first. Just continue to reassure yourself. This can be even more effective if you talk to yourself in the third person. For example, I might say to myself,

Helly, you are resting and relaxing because this is your future life you are working towards and you want to be able to sit, rest and relax whenever you like. Helly, you are safe and you are an ED-bashing superstar!

Yes, it sounds nuts to speak to yourself in this way but it will help lower your anxiety. It will also support your brain's rewiring as your brain recognises that this new behaviour is safe and important.

8. Use food to help your anxiety

Did you think that more food wasn't going to be on the list?

Yep, even with a restrictive eating disorder, eating can help with anxiety.

I can't count how many times people have said to me that when their anxiety rises, if they eat a *fear* food they find that their anxiety rapidly reduces. This is despite convincing thoughts that the opposite will be true or that they will *pay for it later* if they do eat now.

The reason this happens is that a brain on high alert doesn't believe it's safe to sit and eat because a grizzly bear might attack you if you do. When you do sit and eat, despite high anxiety, it sends a message to your brain that it's safe to rest here. Your brain will then switch off the fear response and you then feel calmer to continue to sit, relax and munch on that box of doughnuts.

Use food to alleviate the anxiety that rises when you rest and relax and make that food something worthwhile. The more you do, the easier it will be to continue to relax in that moment and to repeat the experience with less anxiety in future.

9. Lockdown

When I was trying to overcome the movement compulsions, I put myself into a form of lockdown. And this was pre-pandemic and before the term *lockdown* had the connotations it has now. Putting yourself into a form of lockdown while you abstain from exercise and movement compulsions can be very effective.

Build a nest or create a comfortable space in your home that's cosy and inviting. Maybe surround it with motivational notes for yourself. If you live with others then tell them that you are in rest mode and not to be disturbed unless it's an emergency or they are bringing food.

Surround yourself with lots of good food in your nest and just let yourself rest, eat and create the space to focus on healing yourself—body, mind and soul.

10. Let the negative emotions in

You already know that overcoming the eating disorder is going to create a rollercoaster ride of emotions as you face the deep inner pain that has built over the years of increasing dopamine deficit and when the eating disorder was a tool to numb anything stressful or unpleasant that has happened to you. It's now time to let the emotions in. You might want to scream and cry. You might be irritable and angry. Unfortunately, you do have to go through this to come out the other side. At times life can feel very dark and it will feel like the pain will never end but remind yourself that everything is transient, no emotions last forever. This pain will end and you can get through it.

Have the tissues ready, warn people you might be snappy for no reason for a while and then ride it out. It's ok to ask for hugs. It's not ok to restrict or exercise to numb it.

11. Allow yourself to enjoy relaxing

We focus a lot on the anxiety and negative emotions that can hit when you try to abstain from compulsive movement but when you do give yourself permission to just rest, relax and eat, it can be a huge relief and very pleasurable. Allow yourself to enjoy being able to fully rest and nourish your body because there's no reason you shouldn't embrace this new-found joy.

12. Music

Listening to music can help you to manage emotions and learn to rest and relax. Play loud songs if you feel angry and want to shout it out or sad songs when you feel low and want a cry. Play relaxing tunes when you just want to feel calmer and chilled. Music can be powerful for both emotional processing and changing your state from one of anxiety to calm.

13. A dirty house is ok

If your lower-level movement hits come from housework or gardening then let it go. Accept that your house might get dirty and that's normal in a lot of homes. You don't need to do the household chores as often as you think you do and at the moment you should be avoiding them as much as possible to allow the brain reprogramming to work its magic. Let other people do it for you. It might not be up to your standard but that's something else to learn to accept and chill out about!

14. Eradicate other ways you find to move & exercise

Sit down and identify all the other things you engage in to keep yourself moving and busy. Then problem solve how you will address them.

Examples include:

- take public transport or the car rather than walk or cycle

- get a dog walker

- get a gardener

- use the dishwasher instead of washing up

Yes, some of these things mean spending more money at the moment but this is your future at stake. See it as an investment. It has to be worth it to not live in the chains of the illness any longer. Plus it will rewire some of your scarcity mindset beliefs too (see Chapter 34).

15. Ditch the Fitbit

If you have any exercise trackers or a Fitbit then please just throw them away or sell them. They are not at all needed. Aim instead to take as few steps as possible every day but you don't need to track this.

16. Get out to coffee shops

Coffee shops can be invaluable as a means to get out of the house in a positive way. Find a local coffee shop, drive there and order huge calorific drinks and food products that terrify you. Then sit and enjoy being around people and relaxing with food. This also exposes you to the fact that sitting, eating and drinking is very normal human behaviour. And when you are done in the first coffee shop, go to the next. Keep sitting. Keep eating.

17. Sit outside in nature BUT only sitting outside in nature!

Going to sit and relax outside somewhere on a nice day is great if you can trust yourself to just go and sit somewhere. If, on the other hand, it's likely to result in a two hour walk and then ten minute sit down, don't risk it yet and aim for some time in lockdown mode first.

18. You do you

If you have family or other people you live or spend a lot of time with, it's only natural to want to join in on what they are doing. However, if they have decided to go for a family walk or the kids have a swimming trip planned, you have to remind yourself that at this point, you can't join them in the movement side of whatever they are doing. This is a powerful addictive eating disorder you are working to overcome. When you have overcome it, you can choose whether to go on these activities, but at the moment treat this as seriously as you need to and be black-and-white about abstaining from all unnecessary movement until you are free. Family and friends would understand if you had cancer or a broken leg and couldn't join in on everything at the moment and they will understand this too.

19. What would I do if...

Ask yourself, *If this was my last day on this planet, would I spend it moving about compulsively like a demon?* I very much doubt it. Do what you would do. Rest and relax because it really wouldn't matter and the truth is that even though it isn't your last day on this planet (at least I hope it isn't) the movement is still not as important as you think it is.

And Finally

These last points are added at the end because despite their value, they are things that you will have seen recommended widely elsewhere:

- find ways to distract yourself with mindless activities while you are resting and relaxing, e.g. crafts, colouring or journaling

- mindfulness or meditation can be powerful—explore approaches that work for you.

- use affirmations – see Chapter 61

Use as many of the tools given above as you need to ensure that you can move towards fully overcoming the eating disorder, giving up all forms of compulsive movement and learning to rest and relax. Discover the art of being able to treat your body as you would a vulnerable animal or child. These new life skills you develop will allow you to have a much richer, free future.

Chapter 23

Exercise Is a Form of Purging

This is a blog post I wrote a few years ago when I was going through the process to overcome the eating disorder, working hard to address exercise and movement compulsions. The topic is something to reflect on if you do engage in compulsive movement and justify it to yourself as *healthy*. It might also help you if you purge through other behaviours, such as vomiting or laxatives and experience shame about doing so. Other compensatory behaviours shouldn't carry any more shame than exercise and either way, shame is always an inappropriate reaction to any behaviours within a restrictive eating disorder.

Somebody who uses self-induced vomiting or laxatives to compensate for or to manage anxiety after eating is engaging in something difficult for anyone to justify as non-disordered.

Those of us who purge through exercise or lower-level movement can easily hide the behaviour behind seemingly rational excuses... It's 'healthy to move', 'good for mental health', it's a 'nice day', the housework needs doing and so on.

Compulsive movement as a compensatory behaviour is rarely picked up on or seen as essential to treatment in the same way vomiting, laxatives or other forms of purging are.

Instead, movement is seen as a good thing by many: even encouraged. This is despite the fact we are doing it to compensate for eating, it's compulsive, mentally excruciating and an unhealthy way to manage anxiety.

As movement seems to calm us and people hate to see us anxious, the pacing we carry out in a ritualised way, the fact we can't sit down until a certain time or the walks we can't miss aren't challenged. Those around us just accept it as our norm.

Would they, I sometimes wonder, not challenge us if we were carrying out self-induced vomiting in front of them or swallowing a pack of laxatives?

Some might say that this isn't the same and not as serious but IT IS!

Whatever method is used to compensate for eating keeps strong neural pathways live in our brains driving the belief that eating food needs to be compensated for.

We cannot learn new methods to manage anxiety when we continue to engage in disordered ones.

The movement might not be affecting our weight or how much we gain if we are eating enough but it's still a very strong part of the eating disorder and while it's still happening, recovery won't.

So, yes, I believe that exercise and lower-level movement needs to be treated as seriously as purging through vomiting.

We do it for the same reasons, we need to address it in the same way.

Blog post written for RecoveringNomad.com; 2019

Chapter 24

Purging Through Vomiting, Laxatives or Diuretics

There are a number of purging behaviours that people can engage in as part of a restrictive eating disorder. Any forms of purging carry significant risks and they can all be equally addictive and hard to stop. This section is for anyone affected by purging through self-induced vomiting, laxatives or the use of diuretics.

Rates of people with restrictive eating disorders who use self-induced vomiting as a purging method are reported to be somewhere between 56.6% and 86.4%[1]. For laxative use, it's between 26.4% and 56.3% and for diuretics around 49.1%. Up to half of people use more than one of these methods. Some of these figures might seem high and this is perhaps because the studies that reported these rates focused on groups of people with known bulimic tendencies, so those with an exclusive restrictive pattern might have been missed. These figures are included here to show that these behaviours aren't uncommon, which I hope can help to alleviate any shame you might hold if you do engage in any of these forms of purging and haven't felt able to speak to anyone about it.

There are other drugs or ingested substances that can be abused as a way to compensate for eating, including diet pills, amongst others. These aren't all included in the book (as it wasn't practical to do so) but if you do use any other substances, please learn about the risks to them, seek support from someone you trust and speak to your doctor about how to safely stop them.

The Health Risks of Self-Induced Vomiting

As with all purging behaviours, self-induced vomiting comes with significant health risks. In fact, it's reported to carry the highest medical risks.

Repeated vomiting can result in dehydration and loss of electrolytes, including potassium, which is essential for heart function. Low potassium can cause arrhythmias and in some cases cardiac arrest and death.

Other physical consequences of self-induced vomiting include:

- subconjunctival haemorrhages (small bleeds to the eyes)

- dental problems, arising from stomach acid—including enamel erosion, sensitive teeth and gums, caries, gum recession and dental lesions

- parotid gland swelling (the salivary gland located near the mouth and ear), which tends to occur in the days after self-induced vomiting stops and can be painful but will normalise with ongoing cessation of vomiting behaviours

- heartburn, oesophagitis and reflux disease which are caused by stomach acid irritating or damaging the lining of the oesophagus

- voice hoarseness (also due to irritation from stomach acid)

- other stomach complications, including hernias, stomach bleeds and constipation.

The Health Risks of Laxative Abuse

There are several different types of laxatives which work in different ways and some carry more risk than others, but all laxatives, if used excessively and abused, come with health risks. These include:

- electrolyte imbalances

- affecting the ability of your bowel to function normally in the long term—a particular risk with stimulant laxatives

- impaired kidney function

- increased risk of kidney stones

- an increased risk of colorectal cancer

- a risk of cardiac arrest, seizures and arrhythmias, often caused by changes in potassium levels

- chronic or nocturnal diarrhoea

- long term laxative dependence

- stomach pain and tenderness

- possible pancreatic damage

- overuse of senna can lead to liver failure.

The Health Risks of Diuretic Abuse

Diuretics are usually prescribed to people with high blood pressure or heart failure. They work on the kidneys to excrete fluid from the body. Taking diuretics when you don't need them comes with some potentially serious health risks. These include:

- severe electrolyte imbalances

- low blood pressure

- kidney failure to the extent that some people need dialysis

- risk of cardiac arrest and seizures

- low potassium with all the same associated risks as from laxative abuse and vomiting

- muscle weakness due to the break down of muscle tissue from dehydration and low potassium.

As you can see, any forms of purging come with very significant health risks. It can be easy to think that a few episodes of self-induced vomiting won't hurt or that taking a couple of innocent-looking pills can't do any harm. However, that's not the case. This information isn't given here to scare you and I'm sure that you are all too familiar with these risks already. But the reality of how significant the risks are can often be forgotten or buried beneath layers of self-denial when you are entrenched in an addicted, eating disordered brain.

The reality is that these purging behaviours are also highly addictive to someone with a restrictive eating disorder. Just stopping them without support is going to be extremely hard. You will need support and medical monitoring. In the case of laxatives and diuretics, it's strongly recommended you seek medical support and advice for how you can reduce them and come off them safely, while you also work on abstaining from the other eating disordered behaviours that you have.

Advice for Stopping Self-Induced Vomiting

While laxatives, diuretics and diet pills necessitate medical advice on how to stop them, self-induced vomiting is a purging behaviour that you can address now, although you will still need support as you do so. Regular medical monitoring of your blood levels and intermittent heart monitoring is also advised.

Self-induced vomiting is a highly addictive behaviour and it won't be easy to stop. As explained in *Addicted to Energy Deficit*, the act of purging by vomiting not only releases a surge of dopamine but also natural opioids, which your brain can also develop a dependence on as these create intense feelings of pleasure, even euphoria, alongside a state of deep calm.

The first step then in stopping self-induced vomiting is to talk to someone and be open about it. Any addiction thrives in shame and secrecy. There's nothing to be ashamed of in the behaviour and you need help to overcome it. As with restrictive eating, exercise, lower-level movement and some of the addictive rituals people can be affected by, I advise abstaining from self-induced vomiting from the beginning. Of course, it won't be easy but it's the best way to fully overcome it, achieving optimal brain re-programming and physical healing.

Below are some more tips to help you stop purging by vomiting:

- After eating, sit with the discomfort and give yourself an initial time limit in which you won't purge, such as an hour. Once that first hour has passed, deal with the next hour and focus on getting through one hour at a time;

- Be with people who know about your situation and support you. People who will notice and even challenge you if you do disappear to purge. This helps with accountability;

- Develop a new routine for after you eat—something that you will do to stay distracted but that's not driven by the eating disorder. Please don't start going for walks after every meal or snack! It might be that you call a friend, start knitting or doing a jigsaw, journal, learn a new skill or watch an episode of your favourite binge-worthy show;

- Avoid consuming too much water with your meals or snacks;

- Remind yourself that purging now will make you feel better in the short term but it will only make you more sick, anxious and unhappy beyond today;

- Remind yourself regularly of the very real and serious health risks of self-induced vomiting, including the risk of death. You don't want to be that kind of statistic;

- Even if you are home alone, imagine how it would feel if someone did walk in on you purging, whether it was a family member, your child, partner, a friend or your boss. Use it as motivation not to continue this habit now;

- Scream, shout or punch a pillow if it helps to let the frustration out;

- Play loud music to let out anger or frustration or perhaps something quieter that calms you;

- Cry if you need to;

- Recognise every time you don't purge after eating and feel proud of your success, aiming for more;

- And... eat more! As with any form of compensatory behaviour, if you eat more when the urge to engage in it strikes, you will help to unwire the old brain circuits driving restriction and compensatory behaviours while creating new circuits for which food intake, even a lot of food intake, has no link to any form of compensation.

---

1. Forney KJ, Buchman-Schmitt JM, Keel PK, Frank GK. The medical complications associated with purging. Int J Eat Disord. 2016 Mar;49(3):249-59. doi: 10.1002/eat.22504. Epub 2016 Feb 15. PMID: 26876429; PMCID: PMC4803618.

Chapter 25

Chewing & Spitting

C hewing and spitting is another behaviour that's not uncommon in people with restrictive eating disorders, although it's not as commonly spoken about. This is when you chew a food, usually one that's highly palatable and calorie dense, and spit it out before swallowing to avoid ingesting the calories. In this way, it's associated with your addiction to energy deficit and compulsive drive to restrict your intake.

Research suggests that over a third of people with restrictive eating disorders engage in chewing and spitting patterns at some point[12]. Some professionals consider chewing and spitting disorder as a separate form of eating disorder. However, as it's associated with a drive to restrict food intake and in most cases sits alongside other compensatory behaviours, it clearly falls under the restrictive eating disorder umbrella.

The urges to chew and spit come from mixed signalling from your brain. You seek the pleasure and reward from enjoying the taste and sensations that come through chewing foods, while still maintaining the calming or numbing effects that the pursuit of restriction and energy deficit give you. For some people, chewing and spitting is used as a substitute for binge and purge behaviours. Some studies have found that people who use chewing and spitting experience negative emotions afterwards, including self-disgust, remorse and shame but that these can be less distressing than those arising from binging and purging[3].

If you do or have engaged in chewing and spitting behaviours then please know that there's no shame to it. As with any other compensatory or eating disordered behaviour, it's driven by a very powerful brain-based addiction to energy deficit. One of the first steps to take to address it, if you can, is to confide in someone you trust, whether that's someone close to you or a professional or coach. Removing the secretive nature of the behaviour will help to address any shame or guilt you have around it. The next thing to do is decide how to address it. As with any of these behaviours, it will improve as you abstain from restriction and emerge from energy deficit. But conscious focus and some practical measures to abstain from the chewing and spitting behaviours will also be required so that your brain can reprogram and build new non-disordered circuits and networks.

If you have patterns or rituals surrounding chewing and spitting behaviours, reflect on what these are. If it happens at the same time on a particular day of the week or when you are in a specific situation, such as when your partner is out of the house, then find barriers to stop yourself from engaging at these times. This might be inviting someone over, phoning a relative at that time or making other plans that will stop you from following your usual pattern. If you always use the same foods when you chew and spit, avoid buying these and buy other highly palatable dense foods to eat instead that don't have the association with chewing and spitting.

Of course though, you will also need to be very determined and committed.

Remind yourself that you have abstained from restriction and so you will fully consume all the foods you are thinking about and are hungry for. Embrace the weight gain and avoid allowing this to be a reason to spit rather than consume the foods. Remind yourself that you are aiming for overshoot and as ever, stay focused on the bigger picture of what life without an eating disorder can bring you.

---

1. Makhzoumi SH, Guarda AS, Schreyer CC, Reinblatt SP, Redgrave GW, Coughlin JW. Chewing and spitting: a marker of psychopathology and behavioral severity in inpatients with an eating disorder. Eat Behav. 2015 Apr;17:59-61. doi: 10.1016/j.eatbeh.2014.12.012. Epub 2014 Dec 20. PMID: 25580013

2. Guarda AS, Coughlin JW, Cummings M, Marinilli A, Haug N, Boucher M, Heinberg LJ. Chewing and spitting in eating disorders and its relationship to binge eating. Eat Behav. 2004 Jul;5(3):231-9. doi: 10.1016/j.eatbeh.2004.01.001. PMID: 15135335

3. Aouad P, Hay P, Soh N et al. Chew and spit (CHSP): a systematic review. J Eat Disord. 2016; 4(23). https://doi.org/10.1186/s40337-016-0115-1

Chapter 26

Rituals & Triggers

The addictive nature of a restrictive eating disorder makes any behaviours you engage in that directly lead to or maintain energy deficit highly rewarding to your brain and in themselves addictive. These are your restrictive eating habits and compensatory behaviours. As with any addiction, you will also have related rituals that surround each behaviour and key triggers that make you much more likely to pursue an addictive pattern. When you are abstaining from all your addictive behaviours and the pursuit of energy deficit, it's just as important to address these rituals as it is to identify and manage your triggers.

Addicted to Energy Deficit includes an explanation of the neuroscience behind rituals, the power they have in driving the addiction and why not addressing these deeply ingrained patterns will make it harder to stop your wider behaviours. Rituals can be anything, from a certain time of day that you engage in the addiction, your location or the *tools* you use for it. They can also be emotional, for example, having a ritualistic pattern of becoming upset about something as a reason to pursue the behaviours. They are largely unconscious and you often won't realise your patterns unless something happens to highlight or prevent them. Rituals matter because once you begin to engage in one, your brain will start to follow the pathway in fast pursuit of the full fix it craves from the wider addictive behaviour that typically follows. Therefore, when you can stop yourself from engaging in a ritual, you will have more success in stopping the main behaviours.

Triggers and their impact on an addiction like an eating disorder were also covered in greater detail in *Addicted to Energy Deficit*. Although we need to be careful of how much we use the word *triggers* in daily conversation, triggers in relation to eating disorders, addiction and trauma can be powerful and detrimental. A trigger can be anything that pushes your brain into automatically following the habitual network in pursuit of your *drug* (energy deficit) and the related cascade of behaviours, thoughts and emotions. It can be anything that reminds you of your *drug* or the behaviours that lead to a *hit* from it. A trigger can be a situation, person, place, emotional state, time of day, thought or memory. It has the effect of focusing your attention back onto your addictive behaviours and makes them incredibly attractive to engage in at that moment. Because a trigger stimulates your brain to start to release dopamine in anticipation of the full behaviour, the urges to engage will be strong and not doing so will create intense symptoms of craving. Cravings will manifest as agitation, anxiety and irritability, as well as convincing and obsessive thoughts that will attempt to lure you back into the addictive pursuit.

It's therefore important to know your rituals and triggers and make sure that you focus on them in the process to overcome the eating disorder. The following chapters cover some very common rituals and triggers people with eating disorders can develop and provide advice on how to address these. Find your unique patterns, dig them out and bash them.

Chapter 27

To Weigh or Not To Weigh

A key behaviour with a restrictive eating disorder that can become both ritualistic and a powerful trigger is weighing yourself or being weighed. The age-old dilemma and topic for debate when it comes to overcoming an eating disorder is what do you do with the scales? Do you continue to weigh yourself from time to time? Should you be blind-weighed where someone else weighs you but you don't see the numbers? Do the numbers matter? What impact will they have on your progress to overcome the eating disorder?

Everyone has a different opinion on this and I know it can be anxiety provoking when it becomes yet another way in which you are pulled in different directions. You need to establish what's right for you when it comes to the scales, avoiding pressure from your compulsions or from others, including professionals, to weigh yourself or be weighed if deep down you know it's detrimental to your mindset and ability to make positive changes.

It's likely that because you have a restrictive eating disorder, the question, *Can I weigh myself?* stems from your addiction to energy deficit. When the eating disorder developed and you first noticed the numbers on the scales going down, it will have resulted in a surge of dopamine and feel-good brain chemicals.

These dopamine hits quickly became addictive to your brain and left you highly motivated to see the numbers drop further as your brain's way of securing more hits from energy deficit. This resulted in a greater reward response each time the numbers dropped and a continued drive to get them lower.

The ongoing urge to weigh yourself is therefore most likely to be an addictive habit and continuing to do so will keep firing up the eating disorder brain circuits which drive you to restrict further or engage in more compensatory behaviours. As you know, the best way to overcome an eating disorder is to abstain from all the addictive habits and behaviours that make up the eating disorder for you. This includes stepping on the scales.

Being Weighed in Eating Disorder Treatment

For some, the scale debate is made more difficult because in traditional treatment there's often no debate to be had. The *patient* with the eating disorder is weighed regularly, irrespective of what they want and even though being weighed and subjected to those numbers could be psychologically harmful and impact their ability to overcome the eating disorder. Research studies have found that regular weight checks of patients with eating disorders increase their levels of anxiety and depression and lead to increased body focus and negative body image[1].

Despite this clear evidence that weighing people in the name of treatment could do more harm than good, it remains a widespread practice. People are still being denied treatment from eating disorder services if they ask not to be weighed or not to see the numbers. To me, this is unethical and frustrating. If this happens to you, hold onto your autonomy as much as you can, which might mean advocating for yourself to do whatever will be most helpful for your ability to overcome the eating disorder.

To help you form that judgment, let's dig deeper into whether to step on those scales or not.

Eating Disorders Love Numbers

Knowing numbers, placing importance on them and trying to control them becomes compulsive for a lot of people with restrictive eating disorders. This can relate to numbers on the scale, calories, macros, step-counting and times, amongst other things. Tracking these numbers can take over your life and become a form of compulsive torture. You ultimately need to lose the numbers and any meaning or beliefs you have attributed to them to overcome the eating disorder.

Abstaining from stepping on the scales allows your brain to give up the obsessive pursuit of knowing your weight so that you can detach from the belief that you need to know what it is or whether you are gaining and how fast. It allows you to focus on what's more important—abstaining from restrictive eating and compensatory behaviours and to do so without attempting to control how the numbers change.

If you have ever been told that you need to know your weight while you are gaining to *desensitise* from it then please understand that this view holds little truth. I know of more people who have fully overcome a restrictive eating disorder who did so without stepping on a set of scales in the process than people who did. And once you are fully free of the eating disorder and get there without weighing yourself at all, it's more than likely that if and when you do choose to step on scales in your future, those numbers will be meaningless to you. However, to reach that point, it's necessary to abstain from seeing them for a time so your brain can effectively reprogram.

As I embarked on my last ditch attempt to overcome the eating disorder, I went through a process of deciding if I would weigh myself or not. At this point I hadn't seen a professional in a few years and this attempt to finally be free of the eating disorder was entirely self-directed.

The debate over the scales that I had with myself did give rise to increased anxiety and distress. In hindsight, I know it was the addictive nature of the eating disorder that created the powerful thoughts that continuing to weigh myself and see the numbers might be a good thing. It took some deep mental processing to decide not to look at the scales. If I had watched the numbers change, not only would it have served no purpose but it would have carried an unnecessary risk of impacting on the progress I made.

Below is part of a journal entry I wrote when I was deciding whether or not to weigh myself which highlights the mental processing I went through to determine what to do about the scales—this is a real and raw journal entry so it's haphazard in places!

DITCH THE SCALES

I don't need a number on a machine to tell me if I'm healthy or not. But as well as this there are several other reasons not to face the scales:

– Whether I have made progress in beating the eating disorder is shown in my MENTAL state and NOT my weight.

– If the number rises and I decide that it's 'too fast' then it's triggering or even if the number isn't much higher, it still rolls around in my head and can be all-consuming.

– If I was truly responding to full hunger, both mental and physical, or just fecking eating x000 calories a day, then weight gain and reaching my natural set point weight is inevitable. Seeing a number on a scale will make no difference to what my body needs to do and only risks me trying to manipulate it.

– In response to the argument that I need to know to ensure I keep gaining; well, if I have any doubts about that then I need to eat more. At the end of the day, if I'm not being 100% honest about whether I'm responding to full hunger or not then I'm restricting and that's what needs addressing, not a number on a scale.

– Seeing the numbers brings me right back to treatment and hospital approaches of only aiming for gains of x kg per week, target weights and calculating meaningless BMI's.... It's all BULLSH*T.

– People survived for centuries not knowing what a weight was. I don't need to know.

– Being free of the eating disorder means unrestricted eating and rest to prioritise mental healing and rewiring. If I do this then my body will sort itself out and I don't need to know the numbers.

– Other people weighing themselves or being weighed in recovery is their issue. It's probably leaving them disordered and miserable. Don't compare!

– If I've any doubt that I'm not reaching or overshooting my set point weight then I have to eat and eat to ensure I'm still gaining.

– I aim for pressing thighs, belly rolls, happy cellulite and a very

good clothes size. Numbers are irrelevant.

The scales are triggering and unnecessary. They only ever pull me back into the eating disorder mindset. To weigh myself is to teach my brain that the number on the scales matters when it really doesn't.

Helly's Journal Entry

As you can see, I persuaded myself that the scales had to go. The scales were smashed (quite literally) and I know that was the right decision. The relief I felt when I committed to not knowing my weight was immense. It was then that I understood just how much weighing myself could trigger restrictive and compensatory behaviours both before and after a weigh-in.

The Scale Debate is a Personal Decision

Just because I decided not to weigh myself in overcoming the eating disorder doesn't mean that you have to do the same. This is a personal decision.

As I said above, the majority of people I know who have fully overcome an eating disorder haven't weighed themselves in the process, but a few do or aren't given a choice by their *treatment* teams.

Some people convince themselves that they can weigh themselves and that it doesn't affect them and this could be the case. However, I would also urge you to question whether the number on the scales adds any value or meaning to your process of overcoming the eating disorder?

If you are aiming for full mental state recovery (of which a side effect is weight gain), then the markers of progress you should be looking towards are surely mental state markers, not a number that merely represents the relationship of your body with gravity.

So, perhaps just question what values you are placing on knowing your weight. Are they your true values or are they those of an eating disorder?

For many people, seeing the number on the scale has become hard-wired into their brains as a strong trigger to engaging in restricted eating and compensatory behaviours before and/or after they see the numbers. Continuing to step on the scales is to unnecessarily keep facing this trigger that will fire up the eating disorder circuits and make your ability to abstain from all the other eating disordered behaviours much harder.

There are other situations in which you might be expected to step on a set of scales. Many health professionals (even outside of the eating disorder field) love to weigh their patients. It's a practice that's carried out far too frequently in medical settings when it adds very little value to any clinical decisions. Therefore, if your health professionals are asking to weigh you, you have the right to refuse or to question what benefit it brings to the outcome of their consultation with you. In all likelihood, they will struggle to give you a meaningful answer to that question.

And if it's an eating disorder professional who is insisting on weighing you, then again, I would have discussions with them about the benefits of focusing on your mental state and what's impacting you at this point with your ability to make progress in overcoming the eating disorder. By addressing those issues with you, your body will do what it needs to do, which in all likelihood is gain weight and emerge from energy deficit.

The other argument health professionals might use for weighing you, is that it's for medical monitoring purposes. I would contest this too. Your weight does not give much information about your medical stability. It's very easy to manipulate the numbers on the scale if you choose to and someone can be gaining weight but medically unstable. Blood tests, ECGs (heart tracings) and any symptoms you are experiencing give a much clearer picture of your medical stability than the scales.

If You Do Choose To Weigh Yourself

If you do debate the issue of continuing to weigh yourself and decide to do so, I'd make two small suggestions:

1. Only weigh yourself once a fortnight at an absolute maximum, ideally much less and not on the same day of the week.

2. It's important to teach your brain that higher numbers are a good thing and that a drop in numbers is not what you want. You will likely struggle with this to start with but if you want to change your beliefs about the numbers (and you need to if you are going to see them) then as they rise you need to force positive thoughts that will promote new positive beliefs. Several years ago I was in treatment with a young woman who did very well in overcoming the eating disorder. We had to be weighed weekly and whereas most of us would step on the scales with trepidation and a sense of dread if the numbers had risen, even though we knew they needed to, this young woman would punch the air with victory if the numbers were up and then scuttle off to phone her family with excitement. Little did she realise that her actions will have ensured her brain really wired in positive emotions with weight gain and this is almost certainly one reason she did so well. It's a shame

that treatment professionals don't encourage more of their patients to take on such positive reactions when their weight rises!

To conclude, the choice is individual as to whether to weigh yourself or not in the process of overcoming the eating disorder.

Aside from a few, such as this young woman who took on a great mindset to seeing the numbers rise and ultimately did very well, the majority of people do better by not watching the numbers change.

You know that *goal weights* are inappropriate and that to fully overcome the eating disorder you need to aim for your set point weight, allowing for overshoot. Only your body decides what that weight is and so the numbers don't provide meaningful information.

If you are reading this then I suspect that you are having doubts about the scales. If this is the case then listen to those gut instincts and don't take the risk. If seeing the numbers is negatively impacting your ability to abstain from restrictive eating and compensatory behaviours then let the numbers go. Why make the process harder for yourself?

Stop engaging in behaviours that reinforce to your brain that weight and shape hold more value than they do. Eat, rest, abstain from all your behaviours and reprogram your brain as you aim for overshoot. Trust your body to know what it's doing because it does.

And speaking from personal experience, smashing those fecking scales is truly satisfying!

1. Pacanowski CR, Linde JA, Neumark-Sztainer D. Self-weighing: Help-
   ful or harmful for psychological well-being? A review of the literature.
   Curr Obes Rep. 2015 Mar;4(1):65-72. doi: 10.1007/s13679-015-0142-2.
   PMID: 26627092; PMCID: PMC4729441.

Chapter 28

Calorie Counting & Other Forms of Tracking

Numbers, numbers, numbers. For some people with restrictive eating disorders, numbers take over. Counting becomes an obsession—something that you feel compelled to do several times a day or even several times an hour. Numbers dictate key decisions such as the amount or the types of food you will consume, how much activity you will do or whether you are *allowed* to sit down or go to bed. Decisions that should be based on signals sent from your brain and body are dictated by meaningless numbers.

Counting can also be ritualistic. Perhaps you count at certain times of day or write the numbers down in a particular log and if anything interrupts your patterns, you become agitated and need to start over. Counting habits will also be triggers to wider eating disorder behaviours, such as triggering further restriction or feelings of guilt which in themselves trigger movement or self-induced vomiting behaviours.

If you are impacted by numbers as part of an eating disorder, whether it's calorie counting, macros, fats, steps or any other forms of tracking then you will know just how obsessive it can be and the massive impact it has on you. Counting creates increased anxiety and overwhelming urges to engage in other eating disordered habits and it demands a lot of brain space, impairing your concentration on other, more interesting and important things in life.

The counting and number tracking needs to stop to overcome the eating disorder. You need to find ways to abstain from it, disengage and decide that numbers will no longer hold any power over you. When you do disengage from any forms of habitual tracking or counting, it will make you more able to eat without restriction, stop pursuing other addictive behaviours and enable you to tune into and learn to respond to the signals being sent by your brain and body for food and rest.

Calorie Counting

You can know all the facts that calories on labels are inaccurate and that counting calories is a false science because your body is more complicated in relation to how much energy it gets from food and what it does with that energy than simple calories in vs calories out equations. I don't doubt you also know that daily calorie recommendations dished out by health authorities are deliberately lower than a true *average* adult needs for optimal health. You also know, or at least you do now, that your ultimate goal is to eat with zero restriction to overcome the eating disorder. And, if you were eating with no restriction then the numbers would be irrelevant. Despite being fully aware of all these things, the ritualistic and addictively obsessive nature of calorie counting can make it so hard to stop. This is something I also know too well first-hand.

As with anything though, hard doesn't mean impossible and calorie counting can be overcome. Those numbers can lose their power over you and you can discover the joy of not eating by number but eating by hunger, taste, deliciousness, craving, desire or just because it would be rude not to.

But how do you put the numbers aside when counting has become so automatic that it happens before you realise what you are doing? If you have counted calories for any amount of time, you can probably look at a piece of food without seeing the packet or energy value label and your brain will already be turning it into a number. It's going to take conscious and deliberate focus on breaking those old habits and, as with all the addictive behaviours you address, when you first stop counting calories, it's very likely to create anxiety and agitation, although hopefully, it will come with a sense of relief and taste of freedom too.

Below are some tips on how to stop calorie counting. Aim to stop it fully from the beginning and be determined. You will still find it happens automatically at times but as soon as you notice it has, use a method such as one given below to quickly address it. The more you do, the sooner your brain will stop attempting to lure you back into obsessing over the numbers and they'll lose their power over you.

Tips to Stop Calorie Counting

- Remind yourself that calorie counting is a form of permission seeking to eat. It's a way of checking whether you still have enough *allowance* left for more food. It's generated by hunger and desperation to eat more while still satisfying your addiction to restrictive eating and simultaneously reassuring yourself that you haven't gone *too far* with your intake.

- Reflect on all the reasons that you don't want numbers to rule your life forever and the impact that only being able to eat to numbers has on you. Even if you are less restrictive with those numbers than you were, needing to know the numbers for everything you consume is still limiting in terms of being able to eat out, eat meals cooked for you or enjoy other situations where it's not possible to know the values.

- Tune into your instincts and true hunger and let them guide you to what you really want to eat and how much, refusing to let the numbers have any impact.

- Remove the numbers from anything you can. Dispense packs of things into containers and throw the packets away so you can't keep referring back to them. If this isn't possible then use a black marker and mark over the numbers so they aren't there to see. Yes, you might already know the values of these foods but even if you do, the act of removing them will ensure they are out of your environment and demonstrate to your brain that you no longer want to focus on them.

- If you are in a shop or coffee shop and the labels are displayed prominently then stand back so you can see the food options but not the numbers. Choose what you want, listen to your true instincts and stay determined to make that purchase without letting the numbers impact your decision if and when you do notice them.

- When you do look at the numbers or they jump out at you as they sometimes can and you know they are going to influence your decision of what to have, take the option that has the highest number to ensure you are deliberately making the least restrictive choice. And if there's something there of lower value that you think you would have preferred, you can certainly have that as well.

- Aim to buy foods from places that don't display any energy values or come without packaging, such as delis, bakeries, non-chain coffee shops or restaurants and food markets.

- If you write numbers down then stop.

- Delete any apps or trackers you might use. MyFitnessPal is no one's pal.

- Have a tactic ready for if you do start to count in your head. Either start subtracting 7 repeatedly from 700 or have a song that you start to sing very loudly—ideally something that's meaningful and has motivational energy behind it towards overcoming the eating disorder.

- When you start to count, eat something in that very moment as mindlessly as you can. If you try to count that then put something else in your mouth and repeat until you lose track.

- If you do still track a day or part of a day then always round down, never up. If a food has 360 calories, round it to 300, 790 calories becomes 700 etc.

- If you are really struggling to stop calorie counting and those numbers keep your intake below a certain limit each day, give yourself several days in which you deliberately aim to eat a very high number of calories. Your daily goal should be at least 10,000, ideally more. Make it a game and a competition with yourself. Doing this can provide perspective on how irrelevant the numbers really are and allow them to lose their power over you.

- If you weigh foods then stop. Ditch the kitchen scales.

- Grab foods by the handful, bowlful and plateful so that you have no idea how much you have had.

- Scoop spreads abundantly out the jar or pack.

- Aim to eat randomly and freely, letting go of the structure that keeps the calorie limits so rigid and hard to break.

- Avoid meal plans, structures and food diaries and learn what it means to eat freely, to your wants, needs, cravings and desires.

The fact is that you don't need to ever count calories in your life. One common argument is that *I need to count to know that I'm eating enough.* This mindset held me captive in calorie counting habits for a long time too. But the truth is that if there's any doubt that you are eating enough then you aren't and when you are truly eating enough, the fears that you might not be just fade away. If you need to count to ensure you had enough, you are very likely still desperate to eat more so please, just give yourself that permission.

Other Types of Tracking

When it comes to all the other ways that you might habitually track within the eating disorder, such as steps, distances, other forms of nutrient values, heart rate or other physiological data and everything else besides, the advice is always to abstain. Allow your brain to reprogram and learn that numbers don't matter and to instead become skilled at listening to your body and responding to the signals it's sending.

Some of the tips given for calorie counting can also be adapted to fit the other forms of tracking you engage in. The main advice would be to get rid of any apps and trackers. Delete them from your phone or other devices and throw away or sell the Fitbit, Apple Watch or any other tracking device you use.

Humans are not machines, we don't need to be monitored and tracked. Eradicate any step-counting, or if you can't then turn it around and aim to do as few as you possibly can, getting competitive with yourself as to how few that can be.

Let all the numbers go, stop letting them rule how you live your life and learn to do what all animals should do—listen and respond to your body and the signals it sends. Discover the relief that comes when trackers and eating or moving by number no longer hold any power over you.

Chapter 29

Body Image & Weight Gain

B ody image features strongly in the triggers and rituals to an eating disorder for many people. This is because weight gain is an inevitable side effect to overcoming a restrictive eating disorder and most people have some level of discomfort or even fears around it.

You might have ritualistic patterns, such as body checking or avoidance behaviours, which automatically and subconsciously push you to engage in wider habits related to the eating disorder and pursuit of energy deficit.

Just the thought of gaining weight can be a key trigger to habitual restrictive eating patterns and weight-suppressing behaviours. When you start to gain weight, noticing the changes to your body might be a powerful provocation as your brain attempts everything it can to pull you back. After all, your brain is addicted to energy deficit. Weight gain is taking you away from the *drug* that your brain craves.

But even aside from an eating disorder, a changing body, whether through weight changes or in other ways, requires mental adjustment. Your brain has become very familiar with your current body shape and size, as well as how it feels to live and move in it. Your brain now needs time to become familiar with this changing and growing body. At first, this unfamiliar body is something that it will try to keep drawing your attention to as it's constantly scanning for new or present dangers. Change can mean a threat is present, so your brain needs to be sure that you are alert to any new risks.

One analogy I often use to clarify this point is likening the new weight on your body to having a plaster cast on a limb. If you have fractured a limb and had to wear a plaster cast, you'll know that when you first have the cast applied, it feels strange, heavy and uncomfortable and you have to adjust to moving differently. Your brain is constantly bringing your attention to the cast. After a while though, you stop noticing it. It becomes familiar and a part of you. You learn to move with and accept it. Then, when the cast is removed, it's not the presence of the cast that feels odd but the absence of it. Your limb now feels light and strange, you keep thinking the cast should be there and you have to adjust to having a *normal* limb again. It's the same with weight gain. At first, the weight feels strange and you need to adjust to new sensations in your body but the more you reassure your brain that everything is ok, the sooner it becomes familiar to you.

Therefore, the longer you are in your new body and respond positively each time your brain tries to pull your attention to the new changes, the sooner you will begin to feel comfortable, even confident in this growing, stronger and incredible body of yours. Incredible because it's becoming the you-size it was always meant to be.

But weight changes or not, there are very few people on this planet who don't experience body image-related anxieties to a greater or lesser extent. You are going to need to develop some great tools for addressing the negative body image thoughts, feelings and sensations when they arise. The advantage of doing this is that it will give you better body acceptance than most people ever achieve in their lifetime—something that will make you powerful and resilient in your future. Below are some tips to help you improve your body image and deal with bad body image days.

Tips to Cope with Bad Body Image Days

- If today is a bad body image day, decide to pull on your positive pants and be determined that it won't turn today into a bad day.

- Reflect on what else might be going on. There's often something else that has led your brain to use body image as a trigger to attempt to pull you back further into the eating disorder behaviours and their numbing effects. Identify what might be troubling you so you can work through it:

  - Is there something else in your life causing you stress today?

  - Are you upset about something and trying to numb it?

  - Has something stimulated some memories that have caused you to feel uncomfortable?

  - Is there something coming up you are worrying about?

- Worsening body image is often a trigger to restriction and compensatory behaviours so increase your vigilance around these. Eat more to be very sure that your eating doesn't become more restrictive and stay focused on abstaining from all forms of compensation.

- Dress your body in clothes that make you feel good, things that fit your current size and don't make you feel uncomfortable. Choose styles and colours that you love.

- Feel pride in your body and act like you are proud of it.

- Tell your brain that as it has tried to pull you into negative body image thoughts and feelings, you will flood it with positive body thoughts and self-talk instead. Then do just that.

- Tell your body that you appreciate and are proud of it and are very happy it's growing stronger for you every day. Reassure it that you will continue to nourish and respect it, giving it time to heal and repair. Talk to it with kindness and affection because it deserves it. Give it some loving rubs while you do so.

- Do things that make you feel good in your body. Perhaps get your hair or nails done or have a massage. This can also help rewire the scarcity mindset.

- It might sound strange but laugh at the body discomfort. I'd force myself to laugh at myself, to demonstrate to my brain that this poor body image was not just invalid but even laughable. The added bonus of laughing is it reduces levels of the stress hormone, cortisol, and releases feel-good chemicals like serotonin, oxytocin and endorphins.

- Reflect on what this bigger body gives you. Perhaps you are noticing as you move through this process that you have been able to be more present with your family and friends, you can relax and rest more, have more mental freedom, feel more able to love, focus and be authentically you. All these positives of overcoming an eating disorder are associated with your emergence from energy deficit and your growing body.

- Recognise your values beyond aesthetics. I know that your true values are not what someone looks like, whether they have a six-pack, a thigh gap or can fit into a size six pair of jeans. Remember what your true values are beyond diet culture and thin-spiration and strive towards a life filled with them.

- If you find yourself body checking, measuring, pinching or repeatedly looking in mirrors or photographing yourself, catch yourself doing it and tell yourself, *This is not ok.* Then give the part of your body you were focused on a little rub or pat with some affection attached and say sorry to it (again, sounds mad but the more you do it, the better chance of wiring in body acceptance).

- When you get the feeling of your thighs rubbing closer together than they used to or catch a glimpse of your reflection and don't recognise yourself, remind yourself that it just takes time for your brain to adjust to these changes but it will and so will you. Stay positive about them and all will soon feel happily and naturally normal.

- Use distractions to take your brain away from a hyper-focus on your body and shift your attention to things that you enjoy. This might be a hobby, books, learning something new or chatting with people.

- Listen to your rational self. When your emotions are high with feelings that come with poor body image, such as disgust, anxiety, shame, guilt or greed, it's harder to apply your rational mind. But do all you can to take a step back and engage that rational you. You know that the feelings of body discomfort and these emotions are inappropriate and simple tactics of an addicted brain. Choose how to respond so that you can reprogram your brain even faster.

- Use journaling or talking to someone to reflect and help you to engage your rational side.

- Visualisation is another excellent tool. Visualise yourself in a much bigger body, feeling happy, laughing and exuding confidence. Allow yourself to feel those positive emotions as you do so and let your brain literally see that bigger is very certainly going to be better.

- Stand up straight and strut your awesome self! Act with confidence and your confidence will grow.

- And a little *Feck it* attitude never hurts. It helped me a lot. I'd decide that if I was getting bigger then I might as well enjoy it, so I'd put my feet up and reach for more ice cream.

Bad body image days are always hard. They can also be a risk to the process of overcoming a restrictive eating disorder. You will need to become very self-aware when these automatic thoughts or body-checking triggers are present so that you can notice them and choose a different response.

There are several ways to address days like this, not least to keep eating, resting and abstaining from all your eating disorder habits, so your brain understands that these old thought patterns and triggers are no longer worth using.

And for the final words of this chapter, I'll let the me who was experiencing all of this some years ago speak, with the final part of a blog post I wrote on a bad body image day:

> *Today I acknowledged that the feelings of discomfort about my body were there but I refused to engage with these negative thoughts and emotions and decided instead to instigate positive thoughts—telling my body it was bloody amazing and being grateful that it wasn't still as it once was in this disorder. So, I kept eating, allowing it to keep growing, trusting it to determine and do whatever it needs to help me find freedom.*
>
> Excerpt from a blog post written for RecoveringNomad.com

Chapter 30

The "You Are Looking Well" Comments

Most people you meet only have the best of intentions. They want to be kind and to make other people feel good about themselves, so they often make comments intended as compliments, but which an eating disordered brain turns into a judgment. I'm sure you know what I'm talking about—those comments of,

Wow, you are looking so well!

And even if you've only gained half a pound, with no visible change in your appearance, your brain will have a field day. The thoughts can instantly set in,

They think I've let myself go. They think I've gained too much. I need to restrict.

When you are overcoming the eating disorder and dealing with necessary weight gain, you might dread meeting up with people that you haven't seen since your weight started to rise for fear of what comments they will make about your appearance. The, *You are looking well* comments can be strong triggers to urges back to behaviours that lead to energy deficit and weight loss, especially if you aren't prepared for them. However, as you can't control what people are going to say, you can't keep suppressing your weight if you want to overcome the eating disorder and it's not ideal to live in a box and not see anyone for the rest of your days, you are going to need to face and manage any comments that do come your way.

One approach is to use the radical acceptance technique covered in Chapter 59. If someone comments on your weight and you can feel the eating disordered thoughts escalate, choose to accept the situation for what it is. Accept that you can't change what's happened or what was said but you can choose how to react to it. Don't apply judgment or criticism to the person who made the comments or to yourself for feeling upset by them. Accept that you felt as you did and decide that you can change your interpretation of what was said and move forward.

As I was overcoming the eating disorder, I can remember feeling anxious about potential comments from people I hadn't seen since I gained weight. I worried about the impact the comments would have on my urges to restrict or resort to old habits. And I had concerns that others, who had little understanding of eating disorders, would think that because I'd gained some weight, I was now *recovered*. But as with so much in life, the fears were always worse than the reality. I'd either be convinced people would comment and instead they would barely bat an eyelid at my altered appearance, or if they did comment, I'd easily accept it because I knew I had gained weight and that I was on the right path. I could even allow myself to feel pride in my growing body.

My current work with clients who are overcoming restrictive eating disorders and gaining weight has allowed me to observe a regular pattern where the anxiety about potential comments is worse than the actual impact of any comments that are made. In fact, most people become very able to shrug the comments off, take them as compliments, rejoice with close friends that they are becoming human again (and not in a visual way) or feel a sense of pride in their hard work to reach this point. In some cases, people who do meet up with old friends after they have gained significant weight are even disappointed when their friends don't make any comments. But often people won't comment because any visible changes in your body shape or size will barely hit their radar. So, while you are sitting anxiously wondering, *What are they thinking about my size?* the reality is that they are more likely to be too caught up in their own stress or inner insecurities to register what's happening with you.

Don't fear the comments. Be prepared for them so you can choose to radically accept any that do come and receive them with pride as the compliments they were intended to be. If you do receive comments and you notice your thoughts try to pull you back into old habits, recognise what's happening. Then take action—eat and rest in that moment and find someone you can talk to about the situation in a way that will allow you to apply more perspective.

Chapter 31

Habitual Thought Triggers

When you have an eating disorder, it's inevitable that you will have automatic and habitual thought patterns that act as key triggers to your engagement in the eating disorder behaviours. Your brain has learnt that creating these thoughts and any emotions attached to them is an effective way to push you into the pursuit of energy deficit and get the *fix* it craves. Many of these thoughts will be so frequent and habitual that you have little conscious awareness of them, to the point that you engage in the behaviours as soon as the thoughts arise, unaware of what led you into an eating disordered behaviour in that moment.

Specific thought triggers will differ for everyone, although there are some common themes. As you go through the process to overcome the eating disorder, you will need to identify the thoughts and emotions that your brain uses to push you into addictive behaviours. You are then more likely to recognise when they arise so you can choose a new response and move away from your destructive habits.

This is a key time to implement some *If-Then* planning (see Chapter 57). Put in place an *If-Then* plan for each thought you identify. An example of this might be that if the thought that, *I feel bloated today*, would usually lead you to restrict and go for a long walk, you can set up a new response: *If I have the thought that I feel bloated, then I will eat some cookies and lie down while I give my belly a loving massage.*

For every thought you identify, choose an alternative response. The more you engage in the new response and disengage from your previously habitual one, the sooner the new response will become a new non-eating disordered habit.

More examples of typical habitual thought triggers are provided below to help you to identify your specific thought triggers. Not all of them will be relevant to you. Use the examples as a starting guide and list out more of the thoughts that you know regularly impact your progress at bashing out the eating disorder.

Common Habitual Thought Triggers

- I've gained enough weight now. Everyone says I look better so I've gone far enough.

- If I eat this I'll be so anxious about it and uncomfortable later that it will make me want to restrict and compensate. It's not worth the risk.

- It isn't a good time to make changes with eating more or stopping the compensatory behaviours because work is stressful; family are visiting and I won't cope; I don't feel motivated enough or ready; it's a sunny day... Or any number of other reasons your brain uses to delay taking action.

- Carbs make me feel unwell, I have to avoid them (insert relevant food group or type in place of carbs).

- I shouldn't have eaten that, I'm greedy and disgusting.

- I don't have the strength or courage that other people have to overcome this. I can't do it (or other thoughts related to lacking self-belief).

- I can't believe that my life will be any better if I make changes leading to weight gain. I don't see how that could be true.

- I don't know who I'll be if the eating disorder isn't part of my identity.

- My partner/mum/friend isn't being supportive and I can't make changes while they are being like this.

These are just a few examples of the types of thoughts that can instantly trigger eating disorder behaviours. Reflect on what your common thought triggers are, list them and make plans for alternative ways to respond to them. And when your brain gives up using the thoughts it uses now and adopts new tactics (which it will), add these to the list and tackle them too.

Chapter 32

Fat Thoughts & Fear of Weight Gain Stories

L inked to the last chapter but deserving of a chapter of its own are the *fat thoughts* and *fear of weight gain stories* that many of you will be very familiar with. Because of the power that diet culture has in large parts of the world, one of the most effective thought triggers that an eating disorder will use to attempt to keep you in energy deficit are those relating to being *fat*. This isn't true for everyone though—some of you reading this will find that your behaviours and pursuit of energy deficit aren't triggered by thoughts or fears related to weight gain. If this is the case for you then please feel free to skip this chapter.

Addicted to Energy Deficit explains why the common explanation that re- strictive eating disorders are driven by fear of weight gain is misleading. A summary of this is given in the Foreword to this book. I don't believe that you are as afraid of weight gain or being in a bigger body as you believe yourself to be. However, the fear of weight gain narrative has become very compelling and left you with a belief system that encompasses why you feel driven to act in the ways that you do.

To better understand this, you need to be aware that your brain is a prediction machine. It likes to know why things are as they are and will seek a rationale for everything. If it can't find factual information for this, it will use its best guess to create a story. This story will be very believable to you. It will be based on what else is happening, how you are feeling, memories and some cognitive biases. When you became so powerfully addicted to energy deficit, and couldn't stop even though it was having a detrimental effect on your life, your brain sought a narrative for why this was happening. And perhaps your initial dip into energy deficit, which triggered the eating disorder, did arise from a desire to lose weight, as it does for many. It might have been an innocent diet or attempt to exercise more that first pulled you into the addictive grip of the eating disorder. If this is the case, it makes sense that your brain's narrative as to why you haven't been able to stop these weight-suppressing behaviours is that you are, *afraid of weight gain*, or of, *becoming fat*. This narrative will have also been reinforced by a lot of today's popular eating disorder press, which commonly now describes restrictive eating disorders as primarily being a, *fear of weight gain*. Over time, the, *I'm scared of weight gain,* story has become your belief. A belief that reinforces the behaviours and acts as a very effective trigger to your rituals and the energy deficit-seeking habits that you are compelled to pursue.

The *fat thoughts* tie into the fear of weight gain belief system that you might now identify with. The part of your brain that is desperate to hold you captive in the addiction will generate anxiety-provoking and emotionally charged thoughts about being *fat*. These *fat thoughts* are your brain's best weapon to lure you into continued engagement in disordered habits.

Examples of typical *fat* thoughts that you might experience are:

- I'm getting too big

- I can't cope with any more weight gain

- no one will love or respect me if I get fat

- I will feel disgusting if I gain any more weight

- if I get bigger it will look like I've let myself go

- everyone knows that being bigger and gaining weight is unhealthy

- I really don't want to gain more weight

- I want to be thin/slim or look like x person

- I'm just greedy

- people will tease me like they did when I was a child for being big

These thoughts are also emotionally charged, often with associated feelings of shame, regret, disgust, greed, anger and self-hate. This makes them very distressing and because they are so uncomfortable, you seek to quickly numb them with behaviours that lead you towards energy deficit. In this way, you fire up your eating disorder brain network, so the fat thought circuit sparks up the emotional response and these then drive you down the next neural pathways leading you to restrict and use compensatory behaviours. This all happens rapidly and largely unconsciously. Each time this is repeated, which could be many times a day, these neural networks are reinforced.

When you begin to abstain from the eating disordered behaviours and gain weight as you emerge from energy deficit, the *fat thoughts* will likely become more frequent and intense. This is your brain using what has been a fail-safe technique to attempt to lure you back to the behaviours that it finds so rewarding.

You will need every weapon at your disposal to disengage when these thoughts arise, using techniques to turn them into something that speaks of pride in your body and joy at weight gain, engaging in behavioural responses to match. Take action that demonstrates that weight gain is your full intention, aiming for overshoot, so your brain learns that any concerns about weight gain aren't part of your future.

*I want to be clear that I use the word 'fat' here with negative connotations attached to demonstrate the common manner in which people think or talk about weight gain fears. However, I don't believe that fat should have negative connotations attached and I encourage everyone to reframe 'fat' into a wonderful thing, either on your body or in your food!

Chapter 33
Diet Culture & Diet Talk

I couldn't write about common triggers to people with restrictive eating disorders without touching on the subject of diet culture and how frequently you will hear and potentially be affected by diet talk.

The dangers of diet culture, the power of the multi-billion dollar diet industry and the fact that diet culture has roots in racism and white supremacy are all topics that other people have written some excellent books about. I'll leave you to read those if they are topics that interest you. In fact, if you are easily triggered by diet culture then I encourage you to seek out the facts about the diet industry as a way to empower yourself with extra ammunition against its influence.

For context here, some key points about diet culture to be aware of are that because the diet industry is so incredibly rich, it holds immense influence over our governments, health bodies, research institutions, media and just about anything that enables it to become more powerful. It has a vested interest in there being a lot of hype about obesity epidemics, the health risks of weight gain and smaller body types being considered more attractive. It relies on the fact that dieting and weight suppression don't work to ensure people have to keep coming back so that it gets richer. It dictates what research studies get funded so those that would discredit its messages never see the light of day. And of course, it's something that makes overcoming a restrictive eating disorder, which necessitates having to go against so much of what diet culture dictates to be *true,* much harder than it needs to be.

But you can go against diet culture. Yes, it can be triggering to be constantly subjected to diet culture's messages but going against them and deliberately aiming for overshoot will make you not just successful in overcoming this eating disorder but bulletproof to diet culture's B.S. in your future life too. Most people aren't fortunate enough to develop this insight and ability to rise above diet culture in the way that you will.

What then can you do to start to move away from diet culture?

Learn about set point theory and why diets and weight suppression don't work. Understand the reasons that you need to allow your body to restore and find your unique set-point of energy balance with sufficient fat and lean tissue stores. There's a lot of science-based information about this in *Addicted to Energy Deficit.* Arming yourself with this information and returning to it as often as you need to will be invaluable when you see the next advert for some fad diet or *fake-news* report about how weight loss will save everyone from an early death.

Surround yourself with information that supports the things you need to do to overcome the eating disorder. If you use social media, follow health at every size accounts or body-positive influencers who are proving that people are very healthy in plus-size bodies. Seek out communities and friendship groups with people who don't spend their time talking about diets, the gym or weight loss (these people do exist).

Of course though, as much as you try to avoid or recognise the falsities in the diet culture messages that you face in the media, adverts or at the doctors, and aim to spend time with people who aren't into dieting, you will still face occasions when you are exposed to diet talk from the people around you. Diet culture is so much a part of the way people in the Western world live that it's everywhere and people talk about all kinds of things related to it. It's nearly impossible to completely avoid it unless you decide to become a hermit and once again, I don't recommend that. Instead, become bulletproof to it.

Tips to Become Bulletproof to Diet Talk

- Firstly, recognise what's happening. When people around you start talking about their diets, weight loss goals, something they *shouldn't* have eaten, fitness regime or anything else diet related, notice it's happening and remind yourself that this conversation isn't of the least bit of interest or relevance to you.

- Take a deep breath and remember the journey you are on. Quietly remind yourself of the facts about diet culture and its dangers and that you won't be diverted from your path.

- Remember that it's not up to you alone to save the world from diet culture and in this moment, you don't have to fight the diet talk, you just have to protect yourself against it.

- Subtly try and shift the conversation to something far more interesting than what someone looks like, eats or weighs.

- If you feel able to, ask the people present to change the subject to something else. If you are comfortable and want to do so then tell them that you have a history of an eating disorder and this isn't a topic of conversation you ever engage in.

- If you have tried the above and people won't change the topic or take the hint, move away from them, extracting yourself from the situation.

- If you feel passionate about it, tell them why diet culture is so harmful, sharing some facts in a non-confrontational way.

- When you are feeling a bit sassy, grab some doughnuts and happily start munching on them, offering them around pointedly.

- If you are feeling really sassy, proudly declare that you are aiming for weight gain and that you are so happy to no longer be influenced by all the weight loss misinformation in the world as you are now becoming healthier and stronger every day.

- Ask the people with you how many diets they have been on and how many led to long-term success.

- Quietly drop into the conversation some anti-diet statistics. *Did you know that over ninety percent of people who diet regain that weight within five years and two-thirds gain back more than they lost?*

Diet culture and diet talk isn't going to go anywhere fast. I do think it will change over time as more become wise to the diet industry's power and influence but not quickly enough to help you in the coming weeks and months. Therefore, you are going to need to rise above it. It won't be easy but self-awareness is a crucial first step. Recognising when diet culture's messages or diet talk are impacting you and triggering urges to engage in weight-suppressing behaviours will enable you to change your response to the trigger. Not easy but doable. And when you come through this, you will develop the ability to laugh off diet-related conversations and media stories for what they are—irrelevant, disinteresting and not based on facts or your true values.

Chapter 34

The Scarcity Mindset

A scarcity mindset will affect everyone with a restrictive eating disorder in some way. There's a very simple explanation for this. Your body is in a state of energy deficit. When you are in a state of energy deficit, your brain perceives that essential supplies of energy are low. As far as your brain is concerned, this means that other important resources are also in low supply. To your brain, you are in a very scarce environment because if you weren't, why wouldn't you be eating and restoring the energy levels it needs to function optimally?

Of course, you and I know that with a restrictive eating disorder, it's not that food isn't available to you but you have an addiction to energy deficit creating a powerful aversion response to eating enough food to restore you to a state of energy balance. But, as I said, all your brain understands is that not enough food is coming in and so it must be in short supply.

If you really were in a situation in which food and other key resources were in low supply then for your survival it would be very appropriate to:

- stock up on supplies when they are available and before they run out

- use resources you have slowly in case you can't access more

- avoid sharing precious resources with others or giving things away unnecessarily

- ensure that nothing is wasted

- find supplies as economically as you can

- avoid luxuries and unnecessary expenditure

- notice if others have more than you do or where there are abundant resources and possibly steal things to ensure you have enough for your survival

- return anything for a refund that is bought and later deemed unnecessary

- keep earning as much as possible to ensure that resources continue to come in

- save up and keep a *rainy day* fund

- feel stressed and anxious about the fact that food and precious supplies are low

You might recognise aspects of your behaviours in this list. I'd lay bets that when it comes to not just food but to money, time and other significant resources in your life that you experience many of the above *scarcity mindset* symptoms.

In *Addicted to Energy Deficit*, a full description of the Minnesota Starvation Experiment was given. This was when young healthy men were semi-starved for three months during the Second World War to observe the effects hunger can have on a person. The experiment found that the men became hyper-focused on food so they could think about little else. They hated to see food waste, licked their plates, hoarded food and non-food related items and they became more anxious and serious in their demeanour. Two men were observed to shoplift which was completely out of character. These are the effects of food scarcity and what can happen with a scarcity mindset.

The scarcity mindset can impact on so much of your life when you have a restrictive eating disorder and over time it can create even more habits that then need to be addressed as you overcome it. Recognise the scarcity mindset and how it affects you but do so with self-compassion. After all, it's your brain trying to ensure that you survive in an environment in which it perceives famine as real.

The Scarcity Mindset and Food

When it comes to food, the scarcity mindset will impact you in significant ways. As you have a restrictive eating disorder and so by definition eat restrictive amounts to your body's needs, leaving you in a state of energy deficit, you can't not have a food-related scarcity mindset.

The way in which the scarcity mindset with food and eating manifests for you will not be the same as for others because everyone's different. However, there are typical ways in which it presents which include:

- ongoing food thoughts

- putting food on a pedestal—wanting everything you allow yourself to eat to be as perfect as possible so you can savour it

- ritualised eating patterns that make the eating event feel more *special*

- a need to be in the same place to eat; somewhere that your brain has associated with critical food intake and placed high importance on

- hating any interruptions while you eat

- very rigid times of day that you eat—your brain perceives that food is only available at these times and so prioritises them

- feeling a high level of distress if the food you are preparing is ruined, such as if it's burnt or is too hot or cold

- eating very slowly, dragging out the experience to savour it or eating very quickly as your brain fears that the foods available won't be available for long

- a need to stretch out your food supplies, making them last as long as you can, even though you can buy more or have plenty

- hoarding foods, filling the cupboards, freezer and fridge

- feelings of guilt at throwing food away

- hating to see others waste food

- not wanting to share food with other people

- urges to spend time in supermarkets, coffee shops or other food-related places and be around food, even though you won't allow yourself to buy the foods there

- habitual thoughts of wrong-doing when you do buy food, with internal arguments to eat the food that you have at home rather than buying these different items

- possible envy and intrigue at seeing others eat freely and abundantly or strong judgments towards people who eat unrestrictedly, considering them *greedy* or excessive.

There are many ways in which the scarcity mindset in someone in energy deficit will present when it comes to food and these are just some examples. Your food-related scarcity mindset symptoms will largely resolve as you eat and allow yourself all the foods that your brain is asking for.

The Scarcity Mindset and Money Spending

A lot of people with restrictive eating disorders have difficulty spending money. If this is you, you might not have realised that it's a key feature of the scarcity mindset and instead attributed it to your being very careful with money.

Perhaps you struggle to spend money on absolutely anything or it might be you have more difficulty when it comes to spending on yourself or food. Anxiety, overthinking, guilt or even feelings of shame can arise when you try to spend, even when you can more than afford the items and they are essential.

In my case, I could put in hours of painstaking research to find the best price for a pint of milk or bottle of shampoo before finally allowing myself to begrudgingly buy it. If I found something at a great price, I'd buy it in bulk, hoarding supplies, believing that I had to stock up because it might never be this price again. Perhaps you can relate to this. You might also hoard food or non-food related items, feeling compelled to keep enough of certain items in the cupboards. You are possibly an expert at finding supermarket discounts and end-of-the-day mark-downs. Perhaps your family even tease you, as mine did, that you won't buy anything at full price, not realising that this little *quirk* is a symptom of a starved brain.

Money spending can be incredibly hard for people in the scarcity mindset and it's easy to joke about it but it can have a detrimental impact on your life. Even when you can more than afford all the material items and services you need, the ability to spend that money can feel impossible. People with high-paying jobs can still struggle to allow themselves to spend any money. I've known people who haven't bought themselves any new clothes in years. And when they do buy something, the guilt at having done so can become so overwhelming that they return it for a refund. This is life-limiting enough but extend this to other ways in which money needs to be spent to have a fulfilling life. Taking a trip somewhere or going to visit friends and family means you need to spend money to travel there and back and this can be something else that your brain is resistant to. This discomfort then results in your avoidance of going at all. Social activities can be difficult anyway for people with restrictive eating disorders but even more so when you experience guilt at the thought of having to pay for things when you are out, such as food and drinks or entry to a theatre or museum.

We are all very conscious at the moment of rising energy costs but people with restrictive eating disorders in a scarcity mindset can find it hard to use any energy in terms of electricity or gas that they don't deem absolutely necessary. If this affects you, it's likely that you struggle to heat your home to a comfortable level, not because you can't afford to but because your brain is convincing you that you can't or perhaps shouldn't. Living in this way is miserable.

Another way that the scarcity mindset can manifest with money is when it comes to earning and saving. Many with restrictive eating disorders who do work will put in extra hours and think about their earnings and whether they are *enough* to a greater degree than someone who isn't in a scarcity mindset. Most are also excellent at saving any money they can. Of course, this is an important life skill to an extent. Money is important for our current ability to live and it's good to have some savings for the future, but if this saving mentality becomes obsessive or detrimental to your ability to live with enough comfort and freedom now then it needs to be addressed.

You are already aware that restrictive eating and hunger will impact your thoughts, making you think about food a lot of the time as your brain is desperately trying to push you to find the foods it needs. These obsessive thoughts are a symptom of the scarcity mindset and they will extend to all the other important things that your brain perceives as scarce. Despite knowing rationally that you have more than enough money, you might obsess over it and what you can afford more than is *normal* or *healthy*. This can also lead to ruminating thoughts around other things, such as heating resources, fuel in the car or how many teabags you are using, taking your attention from more pleasurable things in life. Happily, as with so much, these constant thoughts and resistance to spending will subside as you emerge from energy deficit and reprogram your brain.

Kleptomania

Kleptomania is the medical term for compulsive stealing. This is always a difficult topic because no one wants to admit to stealing but it can tie into the scarcity mindset.

People with kleptomania feel compelled to steal or shoplift, even when they can easily afford the items they take or don't need them. Afterwards, they can experience guilt, remorse and shame. Studies have found that that there is a strong correlation between people who experience kleptomania and have a diagnosis of a restrictive eating disorder, such as anorexia or bulimia[1]. Some speculate that kleptomania with a restrictive eating disorder results from a compulsive urge to steal, in the same way other eating disordered behaviours are compulsive. Perhaps this is true but it's more likely that stealing initially starts as a result of energy deficit creating a scarcity mindset.

When your brain perceives that there are few essential resources in your environment or that you cannot afford to buy the things you need, it's understandable that in trying to fight for survival and the essentials to stay alive, it will drive you to take what you can. If stealing starts in this way, it can be highly rewarding and trigger a high dopamine release, which then makes these behaviours compulsive.

If you have experienced compulsions to steal or shoplift during the time you have had a restrictive eating disorder, recognise this as a symptom of the scarcity mindset and a brain doing all it can to fight for survival. Remove feelings of guilt and shame from your past actions because you cannot change the past. Those who do experience kleptomania within a restrictive eating disorder largely find the urges to steal subside completely as they emerge from energy deficit. Therefore, the best way to overcome it is to eat, rest, gain weight and get out of the energy deficit state. In the meantime, recognise your patterns if you do have urges to steal or shoplift. Avoid any typical habits or routines that lead you to take things without paying. Shop in different stores because environments can be a trigger to old behaviours. Go shopping with other people so you are less likely to be tempted and if the urge arises when you are in a shop, recognise it and remove yourself from the setting.

If you tend to steal in other situations then set up similar obstacles while you are still overcoming the eating disorder and scarcity mindset.

The Scarcity Mindset and Time

One aspect of your life that you might not have considered as being part of a scarcity mindset is in relation to time. This is the perception or belief that time is always in short supply and so everything has to be done as a priority, leaving you feeling pressured, often overwhelmed and constantly on the go.

It might seem odd that a scarcity mindset caused by food deprivation would stretch over into something like time. However, time is another precious resource that we have and one that can't be replaced. Therefore, your brain will put high importance on it and perceive it to be in short supply because other precious resources are. Plus, when your brain perceives food to be limited, it will create an urgent drive to finish the things that you are doing because it wants you to put your attention back to seeking food and eating.

A time scarcity mindset can present as:

- constantly feeling that time is lacking

- always being on the go but still feeling as if there's so much to do

- feeling pressured by the things you perceive that you need to do, with a sense of urgency, even if they are of little importance

- over-scheduling yourself because you perceive that time will otherwise run out

- rarely switching off each day and being unable to relax

- a belief that if you do slow down, things won't get done and that that would matter

- guilt at the thought of letting others down if you didn't do the things you promise or that they have come to depend on you for

- putting off things you *want* to do for things you feel you *have* to do, keeping you focused on the here and now and not things that matter for your future

- frustration that the things that the authentic you wants to be able to focus on are constantly pushed back for the sake of being busy in other, less meaningful ways.

A time scarcity mindset will improve, at least in part, as you overcome the eating disorder. However, as I wrote about in *Addicted to Energy Deficit*, the drive to be busy and on the go can become compulsive and addictive. It will also impact your ability to put your focus on what matters, which is abstaining from restrictive eating and compensatory behaviours, aiming for overshoot. Therefore it's something you need to focus on and address throughout the process of overcoming the eating disorder. Your priority every day needs to be on doing what you need to do to fully and finally overcome the eating disorder. That should be the most pressing and important thing in your life because, without it, everything else will always be heavily shadowed by your addiction to energy deficit. When you perceive time to be lacking, apply that sense of urgency to getting the eating disorder out of your life.

Tips to Address the Scarcity Mindset

You know that you have a scarcity mindset and that it's significantly impacting your thoughts and behaviours. It has created compulsions and habitual thought patterns above and beyond those directly related to the eating disorder. It stops you from living as freely as you know you could and it contributes to your heightened levels of anxiety, low mood and stress. So how do you address it?

To an extent, the scarcity mindset will resolve as you abstain from the eating disorder, stop chasing energy deficit and pursue energy surplus. This will show your brain that you are no longer in an environment of scarcity. Your brain will perceive that food is available (hurrah!) and so you don't have to stretch out or be overly focused on meagre resources. You will feel much more relaxed about so many things, including food, money and time. This will leave you more laid back and able to live in ways you can't imagine now.

But there will also be some brain reprogramming work to do around the scarcity thoughts and behaviours that are now compulsive and habitual. You will need to address these head-on so that, in the same way as you do with the eating disorder behaviours, you can unwire the old habits and wire in new brain pathways and circuits pursuing thoughts and behaviours that you want. The best way to do this is just the same as with all the other compulsive habits that you want to remove from your life. You abstain from them as much as possible. You need your brain to believe that nothing is scarce now so that you can leave this scarcity mindset behind and move towards an abundance mindset instead.

You have lived restrictively in so many ways for so long, it's now time to live abundantly for a while. Push to the other extreme because it's the quickest and most effective way to get through this.

Let your brain learn that spending money is absolutely fine. Look at your finances with honesty. Consider what you really can afford to spend each week or month on food and non-food-related items. Set yourself minimum spend amounts and give yourself full permission to spend that money. View this not as wasteful and unnecessary but a way to overcome the eating disorder in full, rewiring the scarcity mindset that currently leaves you living a limited life. This is a way to invest in your ability to have a real and positive future. When you do buy yourself something that you wouldn't usually, initial feelings of guilt and regret or shame will come up because they have been automatic and powerful ways your brain has used to stop you from spending money and living freely for a long time. Expect these feelings to come and choose not to engage in them. Then deliberately allow yourself to feel proud that you are doing the best thing for your future and your ability to give back to the world in more meaningful ways than you ever can within the constraints of an eating disorder.

If you have had a habit in the past of returning items after purchase because feelings of guilt kicked in, make yourself a black-and-white rule that you will not only buy yourself new things but you won't return them for a refund. Remove labels from items you buy as soon as you take them home and throw those labels away. Make use of whatever you have bought immediately. Don't leave it in a cupboard or wardrobe for a special occasion or rainy day.

For those of you who are supermarket discount shoppers and end-of-day bargain hunters—push yourself to only buy foods at full price to allow your brain to learn that it's ok to buy things even when they aren't on offer.

Where you always buy economy goods, whether it's food, cosmetics or clothes, allow yourself to buy products at the more luxurious end of the range instead.

If you are someone who rarely visits the hairdresser or barber because of guilt over spending, make yourself regularly visit those who aren't the cheapest but who offer a quality service. Perhaps you have always wanted your nails done or to visit a reflexologist but never allowed yourself—now is the time.

The energy savers amongst you, living in poorly heated homes wearing three jumpers and a coat rather than using the heating, need to start to keep your homes warm and be honest with yourself about what you actually can afford.

If you have hoarded supplies—use up the items you have stockpiled and make a rule for yourself that you can only buy enough supplies for one, maximum two weeks at a time.

And when it comes to time scarcity, make time to relax a priority in your day. Look at all these things you feel so compelled to keep busy doing and prioritise your time to overcoming the eating disorder and doing what's necessary for that. Learning to rest is crucial. This means being able to say no to demands on your time and to realise that so many of the things that you keep busy doing at the moment really can just be left or given to someone else to do.

To Conclude

The scarcity mindset is real and powerful. It will impact all aspects of your life and add to how difficult your life is and the detrimental impact the eating disorder has on it. You need to be aware of how the scarcity mindset impacts you and which parts of your life that you might have attributed to being your little *quirks* are symptoms of your brain perceiving scarcity. Then you need to address it. This will happen in part by abstaining from all the behaviours that create energy deficit but you also need to abstain from the things in your life that stem from a scarcity mindset, aiming for abundance as you do so.

When I was working towards overcoming the eating disorder, one of the first things to worsen if things were sliding backwards were symptoms of the scarcity mindset. Money spending would become more difficult, I'd have more thoughts about whether I could justify petrol costs for a trip or increasingly feel that there just weren't enough hours in the day for all I *had* to do. Therefore, if you are overcoming an eating disorder and you notice that your discomfort with spending money or having enough time is creeping back in, reflect on what's causing it. You have likely slipped back into a greater level of energy deficit and need to step up the eating and abstinence approach once more.

---

1. Grant JE, Chamberlain SR. Symptom severity and its clinical correlates in kleptomania. Ann Clin Psychiatry. 2018 May;30(2):97-101. PMID: 29697710; PMCID: PMC5935224.

Chapter 35

The Return of Emotions & Coping With Feeling Again

An explanation for the way in which emotions can suddenly return when you are overcoming an eating disorder was provided in *Addicted to Energy Deficit*. For many, this is an overwhelming time, especially if it's unexpected.

It helps to be as prepared as you can be for these emotions when they do return. This period of *emotional reawakening* can be a risky time because your automatic and unconscious response to any strong emotion since the eating disorder started has been the addictive behaviours that are so effective at making you feel normal or safely numb again. It is at this time that your best skills in self-awareness and self-reflection will be needed. If you notice your eating disordered urges or thought patterns and self-talk are becoming stronger, take time to reflect on why. Very often it's because something is troubling you that you failed to realise because the eating disorder instantly blocked it.

During the process to overcome the eating disorder, you might find that you go through a period in which you have less interest in life pursuits than you did before. The idea of seeing friends or being around people can suddenly feel exhausting and you might experience an urge to hunker down and avoid the world, in a very different way to the avoidance of social situations that the eating disorder itself created. When this happens, it can be a sign that your brain and body just need to shut down for a while as a form of self-protection. It's often related to a brain that desperately wants to heal, rewire and nutritionally restore which all takes energy, focus and hard work. Therefore it's doing what it can to encourage you to stay home, feel what you need to feel, which might be flat and tearful, and most importantly stop, eat and rest. Feelings and emotions are messages from your brain and body and it's important to recognise, learn from and respond to them without shame or guilt.

What Can You Do to Cope With *Feeling* Emotions Again?

- Allow yourself time and space to let feelings and emotions in and to experience them. Remind yourself that every emotion is real and valid. Don't judge the feelings that come up but begin to develop tools to process them.

- Use your emotions to guide and teach you because that's their purpose. Are they trying to prompt you towards things that might offer comfort, connection or support, or away from things that are causing you pain?

- Avoid immediately reacting to the emotions as they arise. Perhaps you feel anger and immediately want to deal with whatever caused it but take the time to reflect on the appropriate response. Process what you are feeling to establish the best action to take from a less reactive and more reflective state.

- When emotions are high, be alert to their ability to make the eating disorder urges stronger as your automatic way to numb. If you know something is about to happen that will make you emotional or stressed, be prepared that it will trigger more eating disordered thoughts. Be ready for those urges to *lose weight* or body image thoughts to worsen and for the drive to exercise or purge to increase.

- Practise more self-compassion. Treat yourself with more kindness than you usually do. Ask yourself if you would talk to a friend or loved one in the way you talk to yourself, especially when they are going through a hard time. Recognise the pain you are in and talk to yourself without negativity or criticism.

- Talk to others and seek support. This can make the biggest difference. Trust in a friend, partner or family member and talk openly about the emotions coming up. Talking and voicing what you are going through helps label your feelings which is a proven and powerful way to acknowledge and process them, getting them out of your head. Use a coach, therapist or other health professional for this too.

- Learn to be honest and vulnerable with others, trusting them as you do so. Without honesty and vulnerability, relationships and connections to others are superficial. Reflect on how it makes you feel when someone trusts and opens up to you about what's going on for them. It makes you feel connected to them and grateful they felt they could share with you. The people you open up to will also get this same feeling of a stronger connection to you when you do allow yourself to enter that vulnerable but important space. People with eating disorders are great at compassion for others and letting others open up to them but are often bad at allowing themselves to reciprocate. For genuine human connection and to thrive in life, it needs to be a two-way process.

- Many people experience shame. This can be shame of the eating disorder or internal shame of themselves. Shame is painful and you will want to numb it. Ask yourself, would you tell someone else they should be ashamed to have an eating disorder or to experience pain or struggle? I very much doubt it. Apply this same compassion to yourself and again, speak to others to remove the inner judgement. This will help you recognise that others aren't judging you.

- Journaling can be a powerful tool to help reflect on what you are feeling, label what's coming up and process it. See Chapter 63 for more on this.

- Remind yourself that ALL emotions are transient. This is true for good emotions as well as the negative ones. The pain can feel like it will never end when you are in the middle of difficult feelings that you have numbed for so long. But they will end and you will get through them. Remind yourself of this regularly. Use the other tips above, seek support and hold on. Brighter days are ahead.

For some, the process of letting the eating disorder and its addictive habits go will result in emotions that feel too distressing to manage without more support. You might also find as you stop using the eating disorder to block past pain that difficult memories or past trauma begin to resurface. If this happens then please seek out therapy and professional help to process and work through it. Not doing so could prevent you from being able to move beyond the eating disorder or risk switching the addictive drive of the eating disorder to another destructive behaviour as a way to cope.

Finally, if you do find that your emotions have become too strong and you are feeling unsafe or a risk to yourself, please seek urgent help and support. Use emergency services if you need to or mental health helplines appropriate for your country. There is support out there.

Chapter 36

Low Mood & Depression - My Experience

B elow is a blog post that I wrote when I was going through the process to overcome the eating disorder. It's included here to reassure you that these emotions are normal, perhaps even necessary, and that you can come through them.

Lately, I've had more symptoms of depression. This isn't unusual. It would be rare to go through this process without experiencing a low mood.

With an eating disorder, most people have some level of depression. Living a hollow, cold, isolated, tormented & disordered life brings little joy, although we learn to numb it and wear a mask.

In recovery, the true strength of our emotions are felt again. But what's the reason for the lows that can set in?

These are my thoughts:

– *When numbed emotions wake up, it takes time to find new ways to manage them.*

– *As we emerge from an eating disordered fog, we see all that we've missed. We mourn the stolen years—the missed opportunities and relationships. We remember the painful years of torment we endured. The pain of this grief can then act as motivation to persist with recovery.*

– *Depression can make us feel easily overwhelmed, so we slow down, withdraw, turn inwards and act sick. It can force us to rest, focus and let our body and mind function at a more basic level for a while so they can heal.*

– *Recovery is exhausting and relentless. It causes mental and emotional fatigue. It's an ongoing inner conflict of fighting our minds and/or those trying to help us. It's confusing and bewildering.*

– *We experience a deluge of guilt and feelings of wrong-doing when we go against the eating disorder's habits, which only add to the negative emotions we face each day.*

– *The uncertainty of the process adds to a low mood. Why are we going through the pain and will it be worth it? Are we doing recovery 'right'?*

– *There can be comparisons to others who are also trying to overcome an eating disorder, which leads to despair as we fail to reflect on and notice our own progress.*

– Accepting a changing body comes with additional challenges. Mourning the eating disorder body and accepting a healthy but very different appearance is hard. Gaining weight in a society that values thinness is also distressing and confusing.

– Depression can also be a means to seek help if we feel unable to ask for it. It's an obvious sign to others that all is not ok.

– When deep in an eating disorder, we put in a huge amount of effort to appear normal and to be present for the world. In recovery, internal focus is needed in the short term to put every effort into eating, resting and repairing. An appropriate level of depression can help achieve this.

But if you have symptoms of depression, speak to someone and seek the support you need. Depression as you overcome an eating disorder is not uncommon but it can become serious and you shouldn't go through it alone.

Blog post written for RecoveringNomad.com; 2019

Chapter 37

Loneliness

We rarely talk about loneliness but most people will experience it in one form or another when they have an eating disorder or are working to overcome one.

When I was in the process to overcome the eating disorder, I experienced periods of significant loneliness which were worse because I was no longer using the eating disorder to numb the strength of those emotions. It was therefore something I had to learn to work through and not run from. I wrote a blog post at the time about the different forms of loneliness that I'd experienced during the eating disorder. The post is provided below for anyone who is experiencing anything similar now:

> *I'm not ashamed to admit that lately I've been feeling really quite lonely at times and although loneliness is not a new concept in my life, the shape of this current loneliness is different from the ways it's affected me before.*
>
> *This made me reflect more on being lonely—whether we're physically alone or even if we're surrounded by people—loneliness can be a very painful emotion and hard to manage.*

As humans, we are built to be social creatures. Like other mammals, humans evolved to connect to, love, support, nurture and care for one another. A common definition for loneliness is that it occurs when our need for these rewarding social connections or relationships isn't being met.

But, having said that, not everyone who is alone will feel lonely. I am and always have been a person who enjoys and needs time in my own company and I'm often very content by myself and often crave alone time. At other times though, I can and do feel very lonely when I'm alone and at these times it's generally because I'm longing for some form of human contact that isn't available.

When you can understand this definition of loneliness, you can also appreciate why, at times, we can feel lonely even when surrounded by people, if those people aren't meeting our internal needs.

Either way, loneliness is a challenging emotion to manage.

Before developing an eating disorder, I'm fortunate to have rarely felt lonely. I had good and meaningful relationships with family, friends and others and if I needed meaningful contact with another person, I could generally find it. I can only remember a couple of times in my life before the eating disorder when I did experience more acute loneliness and I think the reason they are still so vivid in my memory is because the loneliness was so painful.

Research shows that although loneliness is not a recognised mental illness, it does have a significantly detrimental impact. Lonely people have been found to display signs and symptoms of more acute stress on the whole body than people who aren't lonely and

loneliness is as lethal as smoking fifteen cigarettes a day as lonely
people are 50% more likely to die prematurely[1].

*And those of us with eating disorders are more likely than those
without to experience some form of loneliness on top of all the other
B.S. that the disorder throws at us. So, what forms of loneliness
might we experience with an eating disorder? To answer this I will
speak from my own experiences, some of which might ring true for
you.*

*With the eating disorder, I isolated myself, pushed people away,
avoided social situations and lived alone. This was mainly because of fear of anything that would involve unknown food or
having to sacrifice my rigid and compulsive rituals and behaviours. I wasn't happy, I was incredibly lonely but the eating disorder became the only comfort in my life because the cruel fact of an
eating disorder is that the pain and misery of being lonely is easier
to tolerate than the immensely painful symptoms that come from
addressing it. This form of loneliness when deeply entrenched in
the eating disorder is hard, but the isolation allows the eating
disorder to grow even stronger and as it does so, the numbing effects
it creates can block the true depth of misery. I do remember times
though when I would glimpse into the world that I was no longer
a part of, recognising how cold and miserable I really was. Those
moments still make me weep today.*

*In addition to this, during the eating disorder and as I worked to
overcome it, there were many occasions when I'd be with loved ones
or other people and felt desperate for someone to help and comfort
me. But I'd find it too hard to voice my internal emotions or the
pain I was experiencing and so it would go unnoticed. This was the
worse kind of loneliness, much more so than that experienced from*

actually being alone. Dealing with inner demons that nobody else can understand when in a room full of people is a very lonely situation to find yourself in.

Now I'm on a hopeful road to recovery. I'm feeling alive once again, positive and quite frankly I just want to be out there living life. I don't want to isolate anymore and I want to be around people. But I'm also living alone once again. Suddenly I find myself enjoying the company of others during the day when I'm working or meeting friends, but I also often have free time now in which I crave certain forms of meaningful human contact.

Sadly, due to the years of isolation in the illness, I don't currently have many people to call on to socialise with, be around, talk to and enjoy moments with. I'm doing all the recommended things—avoiding isolating, being around people even if not directly with them and joining social groups but it's going to take time for that meaningful life to build up and in the meantime, it can be quite lonely.

But I also understand that emotions serve a purpose and this feeling of loneliness now is making me take action to escape it, to ensure future weekends are not as lonely as this one.

So I'm sitting with this loneliness today, feeling it and using it. I'm reaching out to people and groups and researching ways to build my life from here. I'm also being vigilant to the fact that the eating disorder can use this loneliness to try to creep back in, offering a numbing blanket from the difficult emotions that are arising and I'm determined not to let it by keeping on top of any urges or compulsions that show up.

Loneliness is painful. It comes in more than one form and at different stages with the eating disorder and in overcoming it. But I think the key is not to let loneliness make the eating disorder stronger. Do all you can not to let the compulsive behaviours gain ground because they numb the hard emotions. Let the feelings of loneliness be there and use them to change your situation in any way possible to lessen the feelings of being lonely. Reach out to people, talk, share and get into the world. Do whatever it takes that doesn't involve allowing the eating disorder to get a look in.

Blog post written for RecoveringNomad.com; 2019

However loneliness affects you, I hope this insight into my experiences can to make you feel less alone in whatever you are going through. Your experiences won't be the same as mine but loneliness as a universal emotion is one we can all relate to. If loneliness is affecting you, it won't last forever. Seek people to talk to. People in your life might not understand what you are going through with the eating disorder and that can make you feel very alone, even if you have people there to support you. But there are people who do understand more, so if you need to, seek them out—whether it's a coach or professional with lived experience, a helpline or a support group. There are people out there who care and who do understand.

---

1. Tiwari SC. Loneliness: A disease? Indian J Psychiatry. 2013 Oct;55(4):320-2. doi: 10.4103/0019-5545.120536. PMID: 24459300; PMCID: PMC3890922.

Chapter 38

I Can't Go On! Recovery Burnout

When you first embark on the journey to overcome the eating disorder, despite some natural trepidation and anxiety, you are also likely to feel energised with hope and even excitement at the thought of all the positive things that can come from it. And this boosts you to make a few life changes, form a support team and feel anxiously exhilarated about the foods you will let yourself eat, the restaurants you might visit, the fun it will bring and the days resting on the couch that you will allow yourself to enjoy.

But let's face it, this process isn't a quick fix. It's long, arduous, exhausting and emotional and requires constant focus and ongoing impulse control when the old habits keep popping in. Along the way, you are likely to feel burnt out. You will crave time out and feel that you can't go on. There are several factors that can lead to this sense of *recovery burnout*.

What Can Lead to Recovery Burnout?

- You have either now conquered some of the foods you were fantasising about eating so they have become routine and safe or you've not yet been able to eat them as freely as you hoped because anxiety and powerful thoughts keep stopping you, so you feel inwardly frustrated.

- The constant anxiety-provoking mental gymnastics of, *If I eat this now, what about later?; I don't want to gain weight; Resting is just me being lazy,* isn't easing and it's exhausting. It's also a sign that you haven't yet managed to let go and fully give in to the necessary eating disorder-bashing action.

- The days you intended to spend eating and resting on the couch haven't happened because it was too easy to let other demands distract and prevent you.

- Or, you've been able to rest fully each day and increased your intake so there's less restriction, but the novelty has worn off, the honeymoon period is over and the seemingly endless days of having to keep intense focus to ensure you're not restricting or engaging in other behaviours feels relentless. And yet you know you can't afford to let your guard down.

- The emotions you've suppressed for years have been taking you on a rollercoaster ride of highs that felt incredible but also lows that are very hard to tolerate, leaving you emotionally drained.

- People around you, who were fully supportive, interested and engaged in your process at the start, have become distracted by their own lives and they've unintentionally dropped the level of support that you still need.

- You are taking slow steps forward but each one feels momentous and creates high anxiety. Deep down you sense that nothing meaningful is changing, creating increased hopelessness.

- Peeling back the eating disorder's numbing effects has left you facing demons that have been buried for years and you've needed to do some very challenging work to address them (if this is the case, I always recommend working with a therapist).

- You've started a journey of self-discovery which has made you aware that you need to build a new identity and make life changes that you know will be worthwhile in the long-term but are daunting and overwhelming to think about putting in place.

- You are holding onto the need to control your body shape, size and weight. This is leading to ongoing mental battles, compulsions and negative thoughts.

Overcoming an eating disorder is comparable to working on a huge project—one that encompasses your whole life and everything in it. But there's no visible and pre-determined endpoint or guarantee of what the results will be. All you have is hope that things will be better than now. It's only natural that working through this process is exhausting and you have times that you feel as if you can't go on. But at the same time, you have now invested in this in all kinds of ways. You know you need to keep moving forward to discover what freedom from the eating disorder is and that going back isn't a feasible option. This is when you feel trapped between a rock and a hard place. Continuing forward seems colossal, but the thought of stopping here or going back also creates feelings of dread, leaving you trapped, almost wishing you hadn't started but still holding that candle of hope that things will improve if you keep going. As much as you want it all to be done or to have a day, week or month off, you know it's not possible.

What do you do then when you are in this position of feeling burnt out, ready to call it quits but still with a glimmer of motivation to keep going?

How to Keep Going Despite Recovery Burnout

- Recognise your progress, big or small. Reflect on where you were when you started, the changes you've made and the shifts that I don't doubt are there. Celebrate the progress because it's real and meaningful.

- Give yourself another pat of recognition that you haven't given up. You feel burnt out but you haven't stopped. Recognise your strength and determination.

- If you feel burnt out because you aren't making big enough changes and feel increasingly hopeless, identify ways to make bigger leaps forward. Where are you still restricting and what other behaviours are you still engaging in, even if to a lesser extent? What rituals are still present? Recognise all the ways that you haven't yet fully abstained from the eating disorder and recommit to full abstinence.

- Big changes are usually easier than small ones to manage, mentally and emotionally. It takes less mental energy and ongoing focus to make those bigger leaps and they also allow for more effective brain reprogramming. Find ways to make bigger changes with challenges that make you zing with fear and a lot of excitement.

- Be daring—Take risks!

- Make the process fun. If you feel bored, stagnant and like you are stuck in a groundhog world of eating, resting and restoring with the honeymoon period truly over, find ways to shake things up and make it fun. One risk in the process is that in changing the routines and habits that drove the eating disorder, you create new routines and habits for recovery but they then stop you from making further progress into addressing every last food rule, behaviour and ritual. Constantly shake up your routines, bring in new and incredible foods and push down the walls of the eating disorder that are still there, allowing yourself to enjoy it.

- Every day ask yourself, *What can I do today that will shake up my day and shake up the eating disorder?* Then do it.

- Keep resting. Avoid getting frustrated or thinking that you *should* be doing more. Resting can be the most productive thing you do. Give yourself that unconditional permission, pushing away thoughts not to.

- If other people in your support team have become less intensively interested in what's happening with you, gently let them know that you might need a bit more support again.

- Explore who you are as the eating disorder dissipates from your life. Let the world of opportunity open up to you and don't be afraid to discover all there is. Talk to people about any thoughts you have about possible life changes and get excited about your future.

- When emotions become overwhelming, allow yourself to feel them, cry, get angry, scream or when it's exhilaration that hits, let it feel incredible. But if it all becomes too much or other deeply buried emotions or memories surface, seek professional support from an appropriate therapist or health professional so you are better able to work through it and move forward.

- Continue to do all you can to work on your body acceptance and body image so you stop consciously or unconsciously attempting to control your size or shape and learn to appreciate it instead.

- Find things each day that are not purely about the eating disorder, but in ways that don't demand too much mental effort and no physical effort. It might be watching Below Deck and getting fully submerged in how ridiculous their lives are.

Burnout in this process is real. It can hit at various stages and it's a risk you need to be aware of. But like anything, knowledge is power and you can manage it, reflecting on why it's there and then shaking things up again so you can move past it, using support to do so.

Chapter 39

I Can't Live With It But I Can't Live Without It

This is a sentence that sums up how it can feel to live with an eating disorder and the moments that you feel frustrated and hopeless in your attempts to overcome it because it's just so hard.

I can't live with it (the eating disorder) but I can't live without it.

It's a bleak place to find yourself. You feel trapped between a rock and a hard place. You hate how much the eating disorder is devastating your life but at the same time, the numbing effects it provides and the ways in which it does serve you are hard to give up.

I clearly remember experiencing this feeling and recognise it regularly in my clients today. Below is part of a journal entry I wrote when I was in the process of overcoming the eating disorder but finding it hard to keep going and I was affected by this state of mind:

I can't face the thought of being fully entrenched in the eating disorder again—going back to the constant hunger and need to keep busy to distract from a miserable and starved existence. Or to be isolated forever more and driven to movement compulsions that inside I'm screaming not to have to do.

But I don't know that I can live with the alternative—not knowing how much bigger I will be, continuing to eat so much food and feeling ok about it, not using movement as a way to numb, block-out hard emotions and distract, and not feeling the calm or even sense of high the eating disorder creates.

But what options do I really have at the moment?

I can go back to the eating disorder in full, let all the behaviours and pursuit of energy deficit continue to calm me but also keep me miserable. Just the thought of doing this fills me with dread and anxiety. Or, I can move forward, let the eating disorder go and find out if things can be different, despite being in a growing body that feels alien and despite everything feeling wrong and complicated to my confused brain.

I suppose deep down I know there is only one right choice and that's to go forward, despite it feeling increasingly uncomfortable and the ever-present powerful thoughts to turn back before it's 'too late'.

But really, 'too late' for what?

Too late to escape the eating disorder controlling me, consuming me and keeping me stuck, isolated and miserable?

Don't I want it to be too late to return to that?

So, despite strong urges to run back, I suppose I do have to override them and move forward all the same.

Helly's Journal Entry

Journaling always helped me apply perspective and consider things with a slightly more rational and less emotional mind. If you feel trapped between a rock and a hard place at the moment, not being able to imagine life being better, no matter which direction you take, just keep moving forwards with blind faith that it will be worth it. It will be.

Chapter 40

It's Not All Bad - The Incredible Side to Eating Disorder Bashing

I'm conscious that a lot of focus has been on the less positive side effects of overcoming an eating disorder, whether they are physical, mental or emotional. This is to ensure you are prepared for them, feel reassured they are normal and help you navigate them when you need to. But I hate to just focus on the negative because there's a side to the process that can also be incredible. The benefits don't just come at the end of the road. They can be there from the beginning and if you adopt a positive mindset throughout the process, you might even find that the negative effects of recovery are outweighed by the positive, possibly amazing aspects.

Your brain is naturally hard-wired through evolution to be biased towards the negatives in life. This is a survival mechanism but it does mean that you have to work extra hard to find and appreciate the positives and even seek ways to deliberately bring more positivity into your mindset, emotions and behaviours. Positivity is also key for effective brain reprogramming (see Chapter 48).

And there are many positives to focus on when you are overcoming an eating disorder. If you can find ways to disengage from the negative self-talk, anxiety and limiting beliefs, then you will be able to see just how much of the process to overcome the eating disorder is and should be positive and even joyful.

Embrace the good things, allowing yourself to proudly appreciate them as you dive into abstaining from the eating disorder and happily and optimistically aim for overshoot.

Where Can You Find the Incredible Side to Eating Disorder-Bashing?

- Initial pride, excitement and hopeful anticipation. You've decided to remove the eating disorder from your life because it's making you miserable. This is a time for incredible optimism.

- Waves of relief, which can hit throughout the process. You don't have to be hungry anymore and you can disengage from all those driven, compulsive and exhausting behaviours and rituals. Doing things you haven't allowed yourself to do for years can also bring additional feelings of gratitude and even more pride.

- A new sense of gratitude and appreciation for all the small things in life that so many people take for granted but that you haven't been able to enjoy for so long, making them feel incredible now.

- Allowing yourself to let go and eat freely and abundantly can feel exhilarating and amazing. Enjoy eating with glee, laughter and joy because food is supposed to be a positive experience and food when you've been hungry and restricted is not just a positive experience, it's incredible.

- Pride of your weight gain and body changes. Feeling positive and grateful that your body is healing after functioning at a basic, deficit state for so long. It's a good thing that your body is now growing and healing for you and it's something to feel thankful for.

- Real laughter. When you are used to feeling numb and you have been fake-laughing for years, you don't even realise how blunted your ability to laugh and enjoy life is. When you experience genuine laughter again, it feels miraculous.

- Rediscovering fun! See Chapter 69 about why fun is so important. Embrace it.

- Feeling as if you are free-falling, which is exhilarating. This can occur for any number of reasons. Embrace these occasions and even seek them out.

- Feeling more present and connected to the people in your life on a deeper level is precious. It will occur more, the further you go in the process.

- The first times that you are with loved ones and friends and not think-ing about food or when you can engage in other behaviours, will make you feel truly connected, calm and at peace.

- Experiencing life beyond your usual groundhog existence; wanting to go on days out, trips and do things for enjoyment; eating out for pleasure and because it's a relaxing and engaging experience and just being fully in the world in ways that feel exciting.

- Looking outside on a grey, cold and rainy day and choosing to stay in and have a duvet day with a large box of chocolates and takeaway because you can and embracing it.

- Finding You. Discovering who you are when you are no longer buried by layers of mask-wearing and eating disorder. Being able to live by your true values, not to the eating disorder's demands and learn what living authentically looks like for you is something to embrace with curiosity and excitement.

There are many incredible aspects to overcoming an eating disorder which you should fully embrace from the beginning. Seek out the positives as you go. Deliberately pursue them and each day actively identify what positive things have happened because you chose recovery. The incredible side to eating disorder-bashing is there and the more you bring it all into your conscious awareness, the more your brain will unconsciously seek more of the same. This is when you begin to feel naturally more positive, hopeful and proud—as you should.

Chapter 41

Side Effects of Overcoming a Restrictive Eating Disorder

An irony of restrictive eating disorders is that when you are fully entrenched in one, living in a state of energy deficit and semi-starvation, you can actually feel pretty darned good. You likely perceive yourself to have high energy levels with a drive to be on the go all the time, rarely feel tired or get sick and find you can sail through your very busy life and numb existence on inadequate food intake. Then you enter the process to overcome the eating disorder and the side effects hit. Suddenly you feel that you are mentally and physically crumbling. This reinforces your belief that you are doing something wrong and were right to think eating more and gaining weight were *unhealthy* for you.

In *Addicted to Energy Deficit*, I provided detailed information about the evolutionary, Flee-from-Famine theory to eating disorders which helps to explain why people with restrictive eating disorders experience a sense of constant high energy from energy deficit, when most people who are energy depleted will feel weak and exhausted. But the drive to be constantly on the go is not a sign of health. It's a sign your body wants you to move to find food.

When you do start to consistently eat more, your brain will switch off the *migratory* response that creates this false energy high. This is when the reality of just how depleted your body is will set in. You might feel like you've been hit by a truck of exhaustion with aches and other symptoms created by a body now doing all it can to heal, restore and repair. When this happens it can be frightening. The inevitable weight gain was already making you feel uncomfortable but you might not have been prepared for all these other symptoms. For any of you about to embark on the process to overcome the eating disorder or going through it at the moment, provided below are some of the side effects that people commonly experience. Next time you wonder, *Does anyone else get this?*, you can refer to this list and know that yes, they do—it's a sign of healing and won't last forever.

Common Side Effects of Overcoming a Restrictive Eating Disorder

Mental & Emotional Effects:

- skin-crawling anxiety that often gets worse before it gets better;

- panic attacks;

- anger, irritability & frustration;

- intense distress and varying degrees of low mood and depression;

- episodes of intense social withdrawal or a general disinterest in life;

- feeling overwhelmed by small things;

- worsening concentration;

- self-disgust, self-loathing and thoughts of failure;

- anxiety at night and nightmares or strange dreams;

- grief, sadness and feelings of loss;

- crying a lot;

- flashbacks to unhappy times when you were deeply entrenched in the eating disorder or other distressing memories;

- more intense and constant thoughts of food, despite eating more than ever;

- urges to drink, smoke, take up drugs or find any other way to manage intense surges in your emotions that hit unexpectedly.

Physical Effects:
- poor sleep;

- fluctuations in hunger and appetite that can swing from one extreme to the other within a few minutes;

- high levels of fatigue & urges to nap;

- body and muscle aches, pains and stiffness;

- nerve pains, including flare-ups of conditions like carpal tunnel syndrome and sciatica (a sign of damaged nerves repairing);

- oedema;

- dizziness;

- vertigo;

- brittle skin, hair and nails which get worse before they get better;

- dry or itchy skin;

- hair falling out;

- constant bloating of varying degrees that can be painful;

- other stomach cramps and pains;

- gas;

- acid reflux;

- constipation or diarrhoea;

- feeling hot all the time;

- night sweats;

- spots or acne;

- blood sugar fluctuations (you are not becoming diabetic);

- shortness of breath and feeling less *fit;*

- swings in hormones and associated symptoms that come with being the equivalent of a hormonal teenager!

No one said that the process to overcome a restrictive eating disorder didn't suck in some quite significant ways. It does. But they say that nothing worth doing in life is easy, so remind yourself that this will be worth it.

Sometimes things have to get worse to get better. It's a bit like when you decide to have a big sort out and tidy up of your house—you have to make more mess and mayhem to get things organised and how you want them. This is your body having a really good sort out to restore. To get to the good part you have to tolerate the messy part. A body trying to heal from any kind of injury or illness creates inflammation, pain, swelling, tiredness and other symptoms to protect itself and to ensure all the right nutrients and chemicals can get to the parts that need fixing. Your job is to let your body do what it needs to do. Keep resting and eating to ensure it has the time and necessary nutrients to do the work. Trust your body because it's on your side.

Chapter 42

Tired & Exhausted

Below is a blog post I wrote when I was in the middle to late stages of overcoming the eating disorder and feeling completely exhausted. I think it effectively sums up what the experience can be like and it might reassure you if you are currently feeling more exhausted than ever.

I am Exhausted.

When I was still caught up in the eating disorder, life was exhausting. Constantly living life to a set of rules, endlessly driven by compulsions and rituals and forever hungry.

Life then was exhausting and miserable but at that time the true depth of the exhaustion wasn't felt.

Now I've moved further towards recovery than ever before and doing so has been emotional and at times even traumatic.

Eating Disorder Bashing is Tiring

Each day spent overcoming the eating disorder feels like another day at war with your mind and those battles, several times a day become boring, yes, but also really tiring.

In the early stages of the process, we and the people around us expect us to be going through difficulties and to be emotional and tired.

But later on, it's less easy for us to be forgiving of ourselves, let alone others forgiving of us when physically we look better, we're seemingly coping with more than our previous narrow existence and yet life is still an intense battle and more exhausting than it has ever felt.

The state of quasi-recovery is one that many struggle to progress from. We appear better and have addressed a lot of restriction and behaviours but still experience regular thoughts, urges and compulsions.

No one wants to stay in quasi-recovery and shouldn't be left to believe that this is the 'best that can be hoped for'. Full freedom from the eating disorder should remain the focus—not a half-life existence. Yet to keep going when it's been a mammoth, exhausting and emotional effort to get this far is a daunting prospect.

Continuing the Marathon from a Quasi-Recovered State

Moving on and continuing to make progress in overcoming the eating disorder when other life demands are escalating makes it feel like the marathon of this process will never end.

Wanting to work and be 'normal' and desperate to be free but at the same time being hit by a train of mental and physical exhaustion makes it challenging to just get through each day with a smile. To do this and to keep pushing ourselves to continue with the work left to do to fully overcome the eating disorder is a demand that's greater than anything faced before.

So yes, the journey of having yet more hurdles to jump to fully restore the body and rewire the brain is ongoing and feels never ending but getting to the absolute finish line also feels more vital than it ever has, yet impossibly far away.

And this is where I find myself. Much better but still not across the finish line and I can't stop until I am.

But I'm exhausted and at times overwhelmed by it all.

Exhausted

Sometimes I feel so worn down that my body hurts and I feel flu-like. Trying to do everything, makes it 100 times harder and the danger is that it becomes all too easy to stay in the damaging fight/flight mode of falsely high energy and low hunger, keeping busy and distracted... until reality hits again.

Yet the thought of not being superhuman and managing to continue this process while working and doing all the other things life asks of me creates feelings of shame, weakness and a sense of having failed yet again.

Perhaps though it's time to admit that I'm just months into recovery from a lengthy and powerful eating disorder and this point I've reached is still early and fragile.

Finding full freedom will naturally take much longer—for my body to completely repair and my brain to fully reprogram. No matter how much of a sprint I try to make this process, some things will just naturally take longer. I have to accept that and be patient.

The Emotional Catch-Up

The other exhausting part at the moment is the emotional catch-up.

When I was entrenched in the eating disorder, emotions were a rarity—good or bad. But now my emotions are stronger and it takes time to develop non-disordered ways to manage the intense emotions as they arise, which they do each day.

At times, waves of memories and pain from things that have happened over the past decade or more come crashing in and emotionally there's more to tolerate and manage than ever.

So, what I'm trying to say is that the exhaustion and the emotions, even at a later stage in overcoming the eating disorder are real and can be intense.

In other difficult life situations, we'd recognise this and practice care and compassion in the expectations we put on ourselves and that others place on us.

Ignoring the Exhaustion is Risky

By ignoring the very real exhaustion that hits, we risk going back to ignoring all our body signals again (including hunger) and to ignore these crucial messages from our body is to re-enter risky territory.

Sometimes, hard though it is, we have to face reality. This process is not yet done.

When I'm exhausted, drained and emotional, it's time to breathe, respect what my body is telling me, allow myself to feel the emotional pain that's arising and not judge this exhaustion or allow shame to keep me stuck but let my body guide. Then keep pushing forwards with what matters most of all... more time for food, rest and healing.

I know that if we let our bodies and brains repair fully and make space for this healing time, that as we cross the finish line, the life options available to be present, give back and make a difference in the world will be infinite and the strength and self-awareness we'll have will make us so powerful.

But now the exhaustion is real and I must respect it.

Blog post written for RecoveringNomad.com; 2020

Chapter 43

Quasi-Recovery - Not Your Endpoint

Quasi-recovery is a concept that's referred to a lot in eating disorder communities but there are mixed interpretations of what it is. I provided my definition of *quasi-recovery* in *Addicted to Energy Deficit:*

Quasi-recovery occurs when you have made some progress along the trajectory of overcoming an eating disorder, where fully consumed by the eating disorder is at one end and fully free of it at the other. Despite your progress, it has now stalled so you are currently treading water. Before this, you made some changes to overcome the eating disorder. Your food intake became less restrictive, and other compensatory behaviours or rituals either reduced, switched or stopped. Mental and physical shifts have occurred, but you are by no means at your potential in terms of fully overcoming the eating disorder and living a life free from it.

Definition of 'quasi-recovery' from Addicted to Energy Deficit

In *Addicted to Energy Deficit*, I also equated quasi-recovery to being trapped in a life of moderation. Your level of restriction or engagement in other behaviours might not be *as bad* or have switched to different energy deficit-creating habits but the habits you still engage in are just as compulsive and the eating disorder remains life-limiting with your pursuit of energy deficit ever-present. In this way, you are just as addicted, only to a moderated level of your *drug*. This is an unhappy place to be, especially when you have made big efforts to overcome the eating disorder and people around you think you are *better* because you have gained a bit of weight or now eat more. But you know you are far from ok and that like this you are at high risk of sliding backwards.

To be honest, all the talk about *quasi-recovery* can be misleading. In quasi-recovery, you still have an active eating disorder. But when you start to think of yourself as being in *quasi-recovery* because you've gained a bit of weight or made some changes to your behaviours or level of restriction, it implies you are now less affected by the eating disorder; whereas your level of addiction to energy deficit might be as crippling as it always was but just manifesting in different ways.

Below is one of the most popular blog posts on my Recovering Nomad website. It's a post I wrote when I decided to deliberately push forward from a quasi-recovered state:

> *Quasi-recovery is a point of no longer being at our worst—mentally or physically—but also not at our full recovery potential.*
>
> *We might have gained weight but we still haven't let go of the eating disorder fully enough to allow our body to gain all the weight it needs to completely repair and function at our set point. Though we have accepted and tolerated the weight gain to now, deep down we remain terrified of gaining another kg.*

We might be eating more, facing fear foods and have broken weird rules and routines regarding how and when we eat but we still have some strict rules and restrictions in place. These can be invisible to those around us and hence easy to deny, even to ourselves.

We might have overcome compulsive movement and exercise so we're no longer the blatantly obsessed movement addict that we once were, but there are still little sneaky habits that we haven't fully let go of just yet, which people around us might even praise and encourage as 'healthy' and yet keep us powerfully compelled to move.

Our lives have opened up from the narrow existence we were living. We can socialise more, be more flexible around people and not just be thinking of doughnuts when someone's holding a conversation with us, but our lives are still not as free as they could and should be.

Quasi-recovery can be a hard place to be.

This stage of recovery is very easy to settle at. It's here that we can fool the world, our family and friends that we are 'recovered' because of how far we've come. But it's still a life lived in eating disorder hell, not completely free or happy. Yet because people around us are so relieved that we're not completely crumbling anymore, we are left and it feels very lonely.

Moving forward from a quasi-recovered state can feel as impossible as the first steps at the beginning of the process.

This time it means making changes with a brain still screaming at us not to gain weight, terrified of facing yet more food and continuing to rest in a world obsessed with movement. But now we're also having to push through with people less understanding of why. This merely adds to our doubts about allowing more weight gain, even though deep down we know it's the only thing that will allow us to fully overcome the eating disorder.

In quasi-recovery, we haven't yet fully reprogrammed our brains and unless we persist with eating unrestrictedly, as well as resting and not manipulating our body weight and shape in other ways, then we never will... which ultimately leaves us either spending years in this half recovered life or going back to full eating disorder hell.

No one wants to stop at a quasi-recovered state, but is it inevitable that we will hit and perhaps tread water at this half-living/semi-recovered state for a time?

Is Quasi-Recovery Inevitable?

The reason I ask this question is that overcoming an eating disorder is a hard, long and often painful process.

We often start from a point of being physically, mentally and emotionally depleted and living in a very cold and disordered inner world.

Muddling our way through the early process of eating and resting more, gaining weight and breaking other rules and behaviours to get this far was distressing, exhausting and at times felt like a form of slow torment and torture.

To have achieved quasi-recovery feels at first like reaching a golden gate from where we've come.

Discovering an ability to live with a bit more meaning, freedom and flexibility, and function more like a normal human—something we might not have experienced for years or decades—can initially feel like a gift in itself.

At this point, don't we deserve a breather and a bit of time to enjoy these early benefits?

Sure we do... but at this point, despite on the surface appearing and feeling better in some ways, underneath the surface it's still a desperate paddle to stay afloat.

And the danger here is that the behaviours and disordered patterns not yet fully eradicated will slowly creep back because we're distracted by enjoying the parts of life we haven't been part of for too long.

Life stress is also a real risk here. When we've used eating disorder behaviours automatically for many years to manage our emotions and cope with stressful life events and we haven't yet fully eradicated them, there's a real danger of sliding back when inevitable life stress hits.

Eventually, in quasi-recovery, the truth that hurts the most is there's still more work to do.

To keep progressing from quasi-recovery means another leap of faith and the possibility of having to face more tears, frustration, distress and turmoil. It's little wonder that so many avoid it and continue half-recovered for years.

But half-recovered isn't living and it's not a state anyone should settle at.

The other danger in quasi-recovery is that we rebuild too much of a life before we are ready and in doing so take fully overcoming the eating disorder off our priority list, not keeping space in our life for the work left to do. But, high on the priority list is very definitely where recovery needs to stay until we are all the way there.

Every one of us has the potential for FULL and not just QUA-SI-recovery. I believe that. But it's hard and painful and it takes a long time to reach the golden gate that represents not a halfway point but the end of the journey.

If you've reached a quasi-recovered state and rested there for a time then don't be hard on yourself. Recovery is exhausting and all-consuming.

Continuing forward though is the only way—heading for your fully free future.

This might mean making more life adjustments to keep overcoming the eating disorder as your priority and it might mean being more determined, stubborn and a bit f**k it when people surrounding you don't understand. But if the simple actions of eating as much as possible, resting and allowing your body to reach its natural weight will break down all the walls of the eating

disorder prison you remain trapped in, then surely it will be worth i
t?

Blog post written for RecoveringNomad.com; 2020

Don't let quasi-recovery, living life in moderation and still being constrained by an eating disorder be your end-point. You can find full freedom but you need to accept that you still have an active restrictive eating disorder, no matter how much more you now eat, how much weight you've gained from your lowest point or what's happening with other behaviours or compulsions. You still need to make big changes to find the freedom you deserve. Seek support and find ways to abstain fully now from all the lingering behaviours and compulsions. You can get beyond this point, just like so many have before you.

And for anyone in the process of overcoming an eating disorder who hasn't reached a point of quasi-recovery—please don't. It's not inevitable that you do. Keep your foot fully on the gas until you reach the end. Use the information here and the experiences of others who did take their foot off the gas or even applied the brakes and regretted it to avoid doing the same.

Chapter 44

The Power of Your Mindset

Your mindset can make or break your ability to bring about meaningful changes. The right mindset will enable you to move beyond negative thought patterns and limiting beliefs, ensuring the action you take is progressive. Features of a helpful mindset include positivity, a determined and *feck-it* attitude, open-mindedness, curiosity and choosing to be a hero!

Are You a Victim or Hero?

> *Abandon the idea that you will forever be the victim of the things that have happened to you. Choose to be a victor.*
>
> Seth Adam Smith

Eating disorders suck. They suck big time and it can be all too easy to fall into an angry and blaming mentality or identify injustices in all directions. It can be easy to ask, *Why me?* fixating on the past and what you did to deserve this fate.

But when you are in this victim mindset of blaming others, traumatic events or past *mistakes*, you are less able to change your situation and become empowered to move forward.

From the stance of a victim you brew resentments, focus on the past with anger and hurt and stop yourself from identifying the changes you need to make to move forward and grow stronger. Anger, hurt, blame and feeling aggrieved are very damaging and stressful emotions to get stuck in, and the person they hurt the most is you.

With a victim mindset, you give yourself the perfect excuse to avoid taking steps forward to overcome the eating disorder. You remove your self-responsibility and empowerment. You let your position as a victim be the reason to stay stuck. That's not to say that the victim mindset is your fault or that you have chosen to adopt this stance. The, *Why me?* mindset is a protective response of the brain. But protective or not, it defers your sense of responsibility to make changes and keeps you trapped in the strength of the eating disorder. And the longer you stay in a victim mindset, the more hard-wired these thoughts and reactions are and the harder it is to move past them—ultimately becoming another thing to rewire.

You didn't deliberately choose a victim mindset but if you recognise this in yourself, you have a choice to move beyond it.

You can choose to let the victim go and be a hero instead.

When you can step away from, *Why me?*, you can grow, heal and look to your future with intent, taking responsibility for yourself. You can leave the past where it belongs and be stronger for it. For some, this might necessitate deeper work with a therapist to be able to move beyond difficult memories or trauma and if that's the case, ensure you are seeking the support to do the necessary work.

Going through life as a hero is about perception. You can accept that life has been less than kind but use your story to grow and become stronger and more resilient. Recognise the positives there are in the world. When old resentments and anger inevitably resurface, remind yourself, *That was then; this is now.* The past makes you who you are today and you can grow from it and because of it.

A time of grief for what has been and what you might have lost is often necessary to heal. Crying can be a part of the healing process as you stop burying your emotions and allow yourself to process them instead. Processing pain is important but getting stuck in blame and anger is not. As individuals, we can be responsible for our thoughts, behaviours and actions, no matter what came before. It's important to accept this as you move away from the victim mindset.

But don't stop at shaking off the victim mindset—replace it with a hero mindset!

What Are the Qualities of a Hero?

A hero is someone with focus, generosity and courage. Determined despite setbacks, finding allies for support and using all resources they have to win. A hero seeks to thrive, not just survive. As a hero, you can inspire yourself and others. Be the person today who lives by their deepest values and become the hero of your own story. This is not denying that life has been hard for you but how you respond to those hardships can make a difference to your future.

Ultimately, the people who are happy and get the most out of life are those who, despite a difficult past, become the hero of their own story and move forward. So, choose not to be a victim of your story. Notice when you are blaming or becoming angry and decide on an alternative response. Use the strength and courage that you do have to change your life.

Perhaps this quote by Paul Coelho sums it up:

> *You can either be a victim of the world or an adventurer in search*
> *of treasure. It all depends on how you view your life.*
>
> Paul Coelho

Many people with distressing life histories become grateful for their past once they are free and living with authenticity and happiness because their past enabled them to become who they are now. Perhaps this will be true for you too.

Curiosity

A curious mindset as you overcome an eating disorder also has benefits. As humans, curiosity is part of our nature. It can propel us into exploratory behaviours, seeking answers to things. The evolutionary function of curiosity is to motivate our learning and optimise our learning experiences, so we are more active in finding answers and internally motivated to do so[1]. To overcome the eating disorder, you know that brain reprogramming and deep learning of new habits, thoughts and beliefs is critical. This is enhanced by a curious mindset.

As well as being beneficial to the deep learning process in overcoming an eating disorder, curiosity can also replace judgments you might hold, and it can help with anxiety. When you can put anxiety to one side and instead adopt curiosity about something that's uncertain in your future, you begin to move towards things with an open mind and less internal resistance. Curiosity was a positive benefit to me when working towards a life free of the eating disorder.

Asking the question, *What will happen if...?* enabled me to view a situation with less fear or trepidation and more intrigue. This made it possible to move towards things I'd otherwise have avoided.

Examples of this were, *What will happen if... I eat huge amounts every single day,* or, *x type of foods,* or, *if I rest much more than I have in years,* or, *if I gain 10lb in a week?*

I began to see the process of overcoming the eating disorder as an experiment, in which I was applying my own method and I'd evaluate the outcomes, remaining open to whatever they would be. Adopting this mindset, with a fun sense of curiosity and playfulness, enabled me to make changes that I'd been otherwise struggling to put in place. I felt excited instead of anxious about the possible outcomes. So, rather than be curious with, *What's the worse that could happen?,* try to foster positivity and a fascination in the process by contemplating what's the best that could happen!

Curiosity is a powerful mindset. Choose to be curious and turn your resistance to changing your habits or facing anxiety-provoking situations into an open sense of wonder.

Be Open-Minded

Tied into the curiosity mindset is being open-minded as you enter and progress through the process of overcoming an eating disorder. Having had an eating disorder for any length of time will have affected your self-identity, thought patterns, beliefs and behaviours. Some aspects of how deeply it's affected your life will be ways that you don't yet realise. Eating disorders don't just numb emotions but they can suppress aspects of who you are and as you let the eating disorder go, it's not uncommon to find your unsuppressed self wants to live a life that's quite different to now.

Examples can be food related—you have been convinced that food choices before were definitely made on preference but then discover that perceived dislikes of certain foods were a subconscious form of restriction and you do quite like them; you might realise that your belief that being busy and on the go is just who you are is also a falsity and you do in fact love nothing more than lying on a sofa with a good book and hot chocolate for the afternoon. It can also stretch into more significant life areas. Perhaps you realise that your career choice isn't one that you feel connected to and decide to have a big change; maybe you realise the eating disorder has been suppressing your ability to connect to your true sexuality or gender identity or that, as you overcome the eating disorder, some relationships that you had thought to be toxic and disconnected from are people you do want in your life.

Stay open-minded to any possibilities relating to who you discover yourself to be and how you choose to live your life as you let the eating disorder go. Be open-minded to whatever comes and stay curious. It can be quite exciting when you think about it, especially when you not only allow the reality in but also find the courage to take the steps to build a life that fully lets you be the truly authentic you.

Feck It, I'm Doing This!

Some might call this mindset bold, but I like to think of this as taking on a *Feck It!* attitude. It's deciding to go for it and let the consequences be whatever they are. It's about not hesitating, not giving fear a second look, being daring and breaking the rules that you need to break to make the changes you need to make. When you get into this determined and positive frame of mind, you are decisively doing whatever there is inner resistance to and as such the anxiety has no room to play so it scarpers.

With the *Feck It* mindset, when someone offers you a slice of cream cake at 10 am, rather than letting your anxiety rise, running for the nearest exit or going into a million mental gymnastics about where you will fit it into other food you planned that day or how you will compensate, you seize the moment and say, *Feck it, why not?.* Then you enjoy the cake, having a second and third helping and continue through the day in the same manner. When your brain is going into spasms about how much weight you will gain because you have dared to sit down for longer today and eaten more, it's saying, *Feck It,* while you put on a second marathon Netflix series, grab another large bag of crisps and order an Indian takeaway.

The *Feck It* attitude is a great way to push forwards because life's too short not to be a bit more daring, while you say *Feck It!*

In bringing all these powerful mindsets together, perhaps it's time to ask yourself,

> *How could this eating disorder and the way it's impacted my life be an opportunity for my future? Who can I be without it and where might being open-minded and curious, with more of a Feck It attitude take me in this world?*

---

1. Kidd C, Hayden BY. The psychology and neuroscience of curiosity. Neuron. 2015 Nov 4;88(3):449-60. doi: 10.1016/j.neuron.2015.09.010. PMID: 26539887; PMCID: PMC4635443.

Chapter 45

Charge into the "Feck No!" Zone & Let Go

Slow and steady is best. You can't manage big leaps. You will become overwhelmed and spiral backwards, undoing the progress you've made.

Don't engage in thoughts like these or let anyone tell you that you can't make big changes to overcome a restrictive eating disorder. You already know that the approach advocated here is to abstain from all possible aspects of the eating disorder and aim for overshoot. And there are explanations, both in this book and in *Addicted to Energy Deficit* as to why this can be the most effective method to not only restore your body but to reprogram your brain and rebuild your life too.

You don't need me to tell you that an eating disorder will build invisible walls of constraint around your life. There are the invisible walls of what you'll let yourself eat, how much, when and where; walls concerning movement, how much you'll allow yourself to rest or what you can tolerate with engaging in or disengaging from other behaviours and rituals. This all creates what might be considered an eating disorder comfort zone, the walls of which can shift over time.

When you are fully entrenched in the eating disorder, the walls will close in on you, constraining you more as they do so. On the flip side, when you make some small changes in addressing the eating disorder, the walls might shift slightly in an outward direction, so you can eat a bit more or sit a bit longer but there's still a barrier—a mental block reinforced by anxiety—as to how far you can go. And no matter how far you might push those walls with the small changes you make, the walls are a constant constraint, suppressing you and your life.

An example of this might be that you can now eat three big meals a day and three decent snacks but if you can't eat a second lunch and six snacks if you wanted to (*Feck no!*), it's still a limited way to exist, effectively living in moderation. Unfortunately, many people find themselves stuck like this, living in moderation for years (see Chapter 43). But I think you want and deserve a life with no walls and no limits: one that's completely free. This means not just pushing at those walls but knocking them down. And it's on the other side that the *Feck No!* zone is found.

Where Do You Find the *Feck No!* Zone?

You have your current eating disorder comfort zone, which might be bigger than it once was but still has walls creating invisible barriers of moderation. These walls represent the rules and limits created by the eating disorder that you can't yet push beyond. The walls can be pushed outward with small changes, each change feeling clunky and wrong at first but easing with each repetition, making your comfort zone grow a little. Of course, you can keep going in this way, gradually nudging those walls out but it will take years. You will get exhausted and it's likely the walls will always remain somewhere within your awareness.

The *Feck No!* zone lies on the other side of the perimeter wall to your eating disorder comfort zone. This is a space, not just of expanded comfort zone, but of complete freedom and liberation because you've embraced full abstinence from every aspect of the eating disorder. This is also a zone that you might not be able to imagine yourself ever stepping into. It's a space that involves food, behaviours and ways of living that strike so much fear in your heart that your head just won't go there, or if it does, it's only with a *Feck No!*

What Can Lurk in the *Feck No!* Zone?

Maybe you can accept weight gain but only to a certain point. *I'll allow myself to gain 50 lbs but not more than this—Feck no!*

Perhaps you can eat McDonald's but it's a *Feck no!* to do so three times a day.

Maybe you up your intake a significant amount but there's still a barrier. *I'm fine to eat 5000 calories but 10,000—Feck no!*

Or perhaps you can eat ice cream in abundance now but only if you can exercise to compensate and you could never lie in bed all day enjoying pints of Ben and Jerry's, even though doing so sounds like bliss.

The reality is that until you find your *Feck no!* zone of eating, living and being, the invisible walls will always be there, keeping you in a state of addicted energy deficit, even if your eating, behaviours and related thoughts are better than they were and you have gained a significant amount of weight. Not breaking into the

Feck no! zone also leaves you holding onto the limiting beliefs and self-talk that maintain the eating disorder.

Entering the *Feck No!* Zone

Taking a blind leap of faith to not just step into but charge into the *Feck no!* zone can be the most exhilarating and liberating moment as you finally feel like the eating disorder is being pushed out in ways you've never experienced or even imagined before.

When you enter the *Feck no!* zone, you fully let go of the eating disorder and in doing so, you don't, as you might tell yourself you have, lose control, you actually GAIN control. The limiting fears or beliefs about *going too far* need to be addressed so you can completely break free.

Don't just nudge at the invisible walls that allow the eating disorder to maintain a hold over you, bulldoze them down.

Let it feel amazing.

When you are in the *Feck no!* zone, anything feels possible, no matter how much weight you gain, or what other consequences of letting the eating disorder go that you thought you'd never cope with happen. You will want to keep going because you have finally found your freedom and ability to live without walls.

Finding your *Feck no!* zone and diving into it feels incredible and it's probably the most important step you will take.

Let your limiting beliefs go and let your fears take a step to one side as you say *Feck it!*, and leap proudly into the *Feck no!* zone. When you do, you'll have no doubts that you are fully capable of overcoming the eating disorder and understand that going back isn't an option. Your confidence will grow and you will become attuned to your inner desires and your authentic, incredible and powerful self.

Chapter 46

Brain Reprogramming

The following chapters provide some tools to enable you to use your current understanding of how your brains work in relation to its capacity for neuroplasticity, habit change and hence reprogramming for your best chance of success with overcoming the eating disorder.

Addicted to Energy Deficit provides a lot of neuroscience about eating disorders, what's happening in an addicted brain and how habits form at a brain-based level, applying this to what needs to happen to reprogram your brain. The coming chapters consider more practical aspects of habit change and brain reprogramming which you can apply in your day-to-day life to secure your free and happy future.

Chapter 47

Enhance Neuroplasticity for Effective Brain Reprogramming

To overcome an eating disorder your brain needs to undergo some significant deep learning. There are very entrenched habits, limiting beliefs, thought patterns and rituals that drive the eating disorder to unwire and new habits, thoughts and beliefs to learn and ultimately wire in. The term, *neuroplasticity,* is used to describe this ability of the brain to change in response to new experiences and learning.

You will probably agree that anything that might help your brain with the deep learning process, enhancing its capacity for neuroplasticity, so that you reprogram faster is worth doing. Some tips are provided below, that if implemented when you are making positive life changes, will enhance your brain's likelihood of rewiring in your chosen direction.

Positivity

Throughout the book I've referred to the importance of remaining positive as you implement changes to overcome the eating disorder. Positivity is also discussed in more detail in the next chapter. But the reason positivity keeps coming up is that your brain will create stronger connections between the relevant neurons if it notices that the new behaviours feel good. Find positivity wherever you can so your brain understands that these new behaviours and thoughts are worth repeating.

Sleep (or Deep Rest)

It's actually during sleep or deep rest that the key structural changes to your brain's wiring occur and not when you are engaged in the new experiences. When you are engaging in a new behaviour or experience that you hope to wire in, the brain cells involved are marked by specific chemicals. It's then when you are asleep that the physical bonds between these marked neurons will form. It's also during sleep that your brain *loses* all the things that happen in your day that it decides it doesn't need to store in longer-term memory. This is another reason why positivity is so important. Your brain needs to understand why it should hold onto the *recovery learning* you've been embarking on each day so that it doesn't decide to *weed* it out during your sleep. Get as much sleep and deep rest as you can when you are overcoming the eating disorder. Your brain needs it to rewire, as much as your body needs it to restore.

Less Stress

Stress, particularly chronic stress, which anyone who has a restrictive eating disorder will experience, affects your brain's structure and function. A study on rats found that those who were put under chronic stress had significant changes to the area of their brain that's responsible for decision-making and goal-directed behaviours[1]. The more stress you are under, the narrower your attention will be and you will be less able to take in new information and less flexible in difficult situations. Therefore, the more stressed you are during the process to overcome the eating disorder, the less able you will be to focus on the necessary action steps and you will be less flexible when trying to process your options in a recovery-based situation. Chronic stress is also known to cause significant shrinkage in the brain's hippocampus, which is the area responsible for processing and storing memories. Having put yourself through some challenging new situations, being able to process and store them as positive memories is important. Therefore, you need to make space in your life for the work to overcome the eating disorder and reduce all non-essential stress—the stress of this process is the essential part! Give your brain the space it needs for the changes you need. If you don't, your brain will struggle to absorb what matters.

Alertness, Focus & Attention

Your brain needs to understand the importance of the new thoughts and behaviours that you are engaging in. You can help your brain understand this by making the active, conscious decision to make the changes you want, focusing on why you are doing them and paying full attention as you engage in them. This will alert your brain to this new *learning*. When your brain is alert and paying attention to your actions, it releases the chemicals epinephrine and acetylcholine, which prime it ready to change. Too many people don't prioritise or appreciate the importance of focus and attention, attempting to change behaviours and build new habits without focusing on what they are doing. But you wouldn't expect your brain to succeed at learning a new language without focusing on your learning. The same applies to learning how to eat without restriction and stop yourself from automatically engaging in purging behaviours. To apply focus, attention and alertness, be conscious of the changes you are making and focused while you do so. You might also use motivational techniques, which could be setting intentions (see Chapter 64), accountability to someone else or some form of emotional motivation. In doing so, your brain is more likely to pay attention to what you are doing and understand that this new path you are asking it to take matters to you.

Challenge, Discomfort & Effort

The more challenge, discomfort and effort you put into any new learning, the more neuroplasticity you get. Changes to your neural connections happen with challenge and exertion, as your brain learns best when things are initially hard, with some resistance. If you've ever been told, *If recovery feels easy then you are not doing it right*, it's true. Rewiring for anything feels uncomfortable and can create agitation and frustration as your brain is being forced down unfamiliar paths. The more attention, challenge and effort you can put into your process, so it's mentally uncomfortable but still possible to pursue, the better your chances of creating the brain changes you want.

Repetition & Persistence

Effective rewiring takes repetition, persistence and ongoing practice. The saying often quoted in eating disorder recovery communities of, *Challenge—Repeat,* exists for a reason. You have to keep using the new pathways you are building or you will lose them. To do something once doesn't embed it in your brain as a new habit. It needs active repetition and if you do stop pursuing the new neural pathways that you are working so hard to wire in, they will be lost.

Patience

There are no quick fixes for neuroplasticity. Consistency and time are key in the process to overcome the eating disorder. You are unlikely to become an excellent driver in two days of learning, no matter how intensive the course, as your brain needs much longer than that to learn all the new skills and habits involved. The same goes for the deep learning needed to overcome the eating disorder (which is also a lot more complicated than learning to drive a car!). You need to give yourself time to keep repeating all the new behaviours and thoughts, remaining consistent as you do. With this, they will gradually become more automatic, until eventually they have wired in and formed new habits.

Transfer New Behaviours to Different Situations

It's all well and good if you get yourself to eat pizza again and you can do so repeatedly with little anxiety or unease. Excellent, well done. However, can you eat any pizza, in any location, at any time of day, with anyone? It's so important in the process that you take the new habits and behaviours you are developing and transfer them to different situations and contexts. Your brain has to learn that these new abilities are not context-dependent. They don't only happen at *safe times* or only at home. You can repeat them anytime and anywhere.

Hydration

Finally, because your brain is made up of 70% water, it works more happily when you are adequately hydrated. Therefore, keep yourself hydrated, with energy-dense drinks to a sensible level and your brain will function all the better for it.

---

1. Dias-Ferreira E, Sousa JC, Melo I, Morgado P, Mesquita AR, Cerqueira JJ, Costa RM, Sousa N. Chronic stress causes frontostriatal reorganization and affects decision-making. Science. 2009 Jul 31;325(5940):621-5. doi: 10.1126/science.1171203. PMID: 19644122.

Chapter 48

Wire Positivity & Purpose into Your Eating Disorder Free Life

The topic of positivity keeps cropping up so it's time to give it a chapter of its own to help you understand how being positive, even if you have to force it at first, can take you further.

As explained in the last chapter, neuroplasticity has more potential for lasting change when you apply positivity to the changes you are making. If you want your brain reprogramming process to happen faster, be more lasting and for your brain to understand that these new behaviours are not just to be endured but that they are a good thing, you need to approach them in the right way.

It's hard to implement positivity when the new experiences you are having feel wrong because of inner resistance generated by anxiety and fear. But why would your brain learn that eating more is a good thing and worth repeating, if when you do so, it's with a focus on thoughts and actions that are telling it the opposite is true?

If you go through the process, barely tolerating it and eating some fear foods but still with a judgemental mindset and belief that these foods are to be feared and endured rather than enjoyed, then your brain won't effectively reprogram and you will hold onto old habits and beliefs created by the eating disorder.

The most likely outcome in this scenario is that despite repeated occasions of eating the anxiety-provoking foods, your brain didn't learn that these foods were a good thing and so once there's less enforcement to keep eating them, it won't seek to repeat the experiences and old habits will rapidly return.

For example, you could eat a tub of Ben and Jerry's each day but if you are doing so by rushing through them, believing it to be wrong and deliberately distracting yourself, then your brain won't look to repeat these experiences because it perceived little reward from them.

Ultimately, brain reprogramming is about repetition of the new behaviours but repetition alone won't change your attitude, mindsets or beliefs. Repetition alone won't establish a positive or lasting future free of the eating disorder because you'll have no motivation to keep going.

It's therefore important to make sure that your experiences to overcome the eating disorder fit with your vision of the positive, exciting and meaningful future that you want, so your brain can reprogram with positivity and purpose.

Below are some steps to implement as you go through the process of overcoming the eating disorder that will show your brain that the new experiences it's encountering are worth repeating. Your brain will then be more likely to wire them in to form happy new habits.

Wiring In Positive, Meaningful & Lasting New Habits

Make your experiences intense

The more intensity that's felt in your body and mind to an experience, the more chance it will be remembered. This is true for negative, as well as positive experiences, although your brain will wire in negative experiences much faster than positive ones. Therefore, you are battling against the current but nothing about this is easy. With more intensity, your neurons release more norepinephrine which makes the connections between them stronger. And when an experience is more pleasurable than your brain anticipated, there will be more dopamine release, which makes the connections between your neurons stronger and it more likely that your brain will seek to repeat the experience. So make your recovery actions richer, fuller, bigger and more intensive in all ways you can. Feel excited, telling yourself how amazing this is and feel the sensations in your body. Notice colours, tastes and textures and be energised with joy and pride.

Make the experience last longer

Focus on not only making the experience feel positive but also on prolonging the good feelings and emotions that you derive from it. When you eat a slice of chocolate cake with lashings of cream, let the resistance and fear be there but focus on the positives of this experience. Notice the incredible taste, the feeling of exhilaration that you are winning, the pride in yourself or seeing a look of joy in a loved one's eyes. Then stay with these feelings and sensations for as long as you can. You want your brain to learn that chocolate cake is a good thing, so show it that's the case. Stay devoted to feeling good about eating that cake for a good 5, 10, 20 seconds or more if you can. Take breaths with long exhalations which will keep you feeling calmer. Tell yourself you feel good, you are a superhero and you're safe. And add in some energising emotions too—delight, awe, curiosity, excitement and full-on bouncing glee. Prolong and notice an eating disorder-bashing experience and it will wire in more intensively than if you let it race by.

Make an experience all-encompassing

Notice the good things about the experiences you are having to overcome the eating disorder as broadly as you can. Let's say you are trying to make yourself sit on the sofa for the afternoon when usually you would be moving or standing. You want your brain to understand that this is a pleasurable experience and one worth repeating. Therefore, avoid sitting on the sofa with a body full of tension and agitation. Instead, make yourself relax into it and notice the good things. Feel the softness of the cushions, the warmth and comfort. Tell yourself this is good and you are safe. Put your feet up and take breaths with slow exhales to make your body relax more. Force into your mind's eye the future you want in which you are a person who does relax and rests at will. And remember that your mind and body are joined and one influences the other. How we act affects how we think and feel and vice versa. Therefore, relaxing your body will help to relax your mind and a smile will tell your brain that things are good. Feel this experience on every incredible level—the sensations, what this experience can bring you and feel safe. Make the experience all-encompassing to reinforce to your brain that turning this into a habit would be no bad thing.

Use novelty

Your brain loves things that are novel and will pay more attention to anything that it doesn't see or do on autopilot every day. This won't be hard to achieve when you first set out to overcome the eating disorder, assuming you are making necessary changes to your behaviours and thoughts. But if you want all this hard work to pay off then start noticing the rewards to all these new things and keep them fresh. Seek rewards that your brain wasn't expecting and it will be more motivated. Don't be passive in this process. Use your mind to actively notice every positive new stimulus as you make all these changes, allowing them to wire into your brain. Even if you have now been working to overcome the eating disorder for longer and some of the new habits you have been building are becoming more familiar, you can still stimulate your brain to embed them more deeply by finding unexpected rewards from them. Perhaps you have been eating big plates of waffles for breakfast for a while now. Next time you have them, notice the delicious taste more than you usually would. Say to yourself, *Wow, I didn't expect this to taste so good*, and your brain will notice. Or keep changing the toppings and how they are prepared. No two experiences are ever the same, so notice the differences. Seek out novelty every day and your brain will motivate you to repeat these great experiences. In this way, the work of overcoming the eating disorder will become much less of an uphill battle.

Make it personal

If you rush to finish a large ice cream sundae, wishing it wasn't happening and rapidly leave the experience then your brain won't pay much attention or store it as something memorable and worth repeating. Your brain isn't interested in things you do or experience each day that aren't of personal relevance to you—it has more important things to focus on. Therefore, as resistant as you feel to the ice cream experience, notice it, be present and make it personally relevant in wonderful ways. Pay attention to why this experience is going to help you and how. Why is eating this ice cream and having this memory valuable to you? Focus on that. Visualise what ice cream experiences like this can bring to your future. And again, stay as relaxed as you can. Tell yourself, *This is right for me; this is what I need and this is bloomin' delicious!* Perhaps you can call to mind times you had relaxed and fun ice cream experiences as a child and store this new memory with those old ones. It can be all too tempting to rush through these experiences when they generate anxiety and resistance, trying not to notice them. However, for your brain reprogramming to be most effective, it needs you to pay attention to each experience and to understand why they matter to you.

Fully embrace all the positives to be found in the experiences you are having to overcome the eating disorder. You might not feel positive about them in the moment, but seek out ways to notice the positives that are there and wallow, not in what's bad or in the anxiety-generated future-tripping thoughts, but in all the great things these experiences hold in the present and will bring to your future. Do this repeatedly and very soon, not only will your brain begin to naturally seek these experiences out, but you will also feel much more positive in yourself.

Chapter 49

Common Pitfalls to Changing Habits

*A*ddicted to Energy Deficit explains some of the neuroscience of habits, alongside steps to take to make and break them, using the habit loop. When you are overcoming an eating disorder, changing your habits demands a lot of focus. You need to abstain from, or at least moderate, old behaviours, thoughts and emotions as you form the new habits that you want in your eating disorder-free life.

When you are putting so much focus and hard work into changing your addictive habits, rituals and compulsions, you will want to be confident it will be effective and worthwhile. This means ensuring that the new brain pathways you build are distinct from your brain's eating disorder network.

Below are some of the most common pitfalls to habit change. Awareness of these will help you to avoid them:

1. **Expecting big results too quickly and not recognising the progress along the way**. Overcoming an eating disorder and fully embedding in new habits takes a long time, a lot of hard work and continuous steps forward. If you focus purely on the endpoint and

whether you are there yet, it's very easy to get discouraged and feel that you should be at the end when you still need to continue to enjoy the journey. Celebrate the wins that you have along the way. Not doing so is the equivalent of a football team striving to win the World Cup but not recognising or celebrating their win in the first qualifying match. Celebrate all the wins, allowing them to motivate you to the next. Because let's face it overcoming an eating disorder is a much harder and bigger win than any World Cup victory!

2. **Inconsistency in your new habits and behaviours**. Habits develop and grow through repetition and consistency. Practising a new behaviour or thought pattern once or twice won't instantly become habitual. Make sure that the new habits you are developing are regularly repeated and that you prioritise them each day. It's all too common for people to push themselves to perhaps change lunch from their habitual restrictive foods and face a whole pizza and ice cream. And they generally feel amazing in the immediate aftermath. But then they don't repeat it and the next day their habitual restrictive lunch is back. Repetition and consistency are key.

3. **Placing more focus on stopping old behaviours rather than creating new ones**. When you abstain from your old habits and behaviours, such as restriction, purging or exercise, it can be very easy to say you will just stop them. But success is unlikely without a plan for positive habits to replace them with. Put in place new, positive habits to develop and reward. You might decide to stop all exercise and you will replace it with sitting down and writing because you have always loved to write but never made time for it or perhaps you will replace it with sitting in a coffee shop and eating cake, sampling every flavour. If you purge, instead of just saying, *I'll stop,* replace the behaviour with something else. You might phone someone after a challenging meal, paint or play loud music. Do whatever works for you and feel proud when you achieve it.

4. **Believing that information alone leads to action.** Knowing why you should stop an old habit and replace it with a new one doesn't equate to doing it. Absorbing information about the process of overcoming an eating disorder by reading, listening or watching eating disorder-related content is fine but it won't change your brain structure. The only way to change your habits and build new brain circuits is to apply the information to your day-to-day life. Transformation into an eating disorder-free superhero isn't a passive process.

5. **Ignoring how much your environment shapes your behaviours.** The environment you expose yourself to can make or break your habits and ability to change them. Your environment, the people around you and the things that you see and hear each day can automatically trigger old habits or if used correctly, prompt you towards the new habits that you want to build. Don't underestimate how much your environment impacts your habit change abilities and make changes to it where you can.

6. **Underestimating the power of triggers.** Triggers to habits are real and powerful, particularly when it comes to addictions. Nothing we do habitually happens without a trigger of some form. Triggers can push you into the habits you want to break or they can help you create new ones. Focus on what your triggers are for old habits and what triggers you can put in place to enable you to change them. An example of this is that your old habit of not eating breakfast until 9 am is one that you want to change. Put food by your bed so you have no excuse not to eat as soon as you wake up at 7 am. Then continue to eat all morning to break all restriction and avoid rigid habitual eating times. Put in place triggers that will push you into new habits with minimal conscious effort.

7. **Focusing on abstract goals rather than concrete behaviours.** To overcome the eating disorder, you might have the goal to, *be fully free*

of the eating disorder. This is great but it's not telling your brain what it needs to do to achieve that. Set goals that are concrete, specific and that lead to that overarching abstract endpoint.

8. **Assuming it will all be too hard.** Very often, people say they want to change and overcome the eating disorder but when asked what they will do to achieve that, they will give suggestions of what they think they *should* do, such as eating a much bigger breakfast, but with an, *If I can,* attached. As soon as the, *If I can,* assumption that it probably won't happen because it will be too darned hard is put in there, it's pretty much guaranteed it won't happen. This is because you have already decided it won't. Develop and nurture confidence in your abilities.

9. **No set time frames for change.** Goals for habit change are one thing but set yourself fixed time frames for those changes, rather than just a vague thought of, *Yeah, I'll do that at some point in the future.* You will have more success with fixed time goals for your habit changes which you can then build on, leading to an increase in your motivation and focus, while preventing things from drifting, as they all too easily can.

Habit change isn't easy, especially when the habits are addictive and compulsive. But be aware of what you need to do, believe you can, set up everything possible to improve your chance of success and very soon those new behaviours you want will be deeply entrenched habits that enable you to live your best life.

Chapter 50

Do an Environmental Survey

S everal factors can affect how successfully you abstain from old habits and reprogram your brain. One of these is your immediate environment.

Addicted to Energy Deficit discusses the power of triggers and how the environments you frequently spend time in can act as significant cues or triggers that automatically and unconsciously drive you to engage in your habits. Therefore, wherever possible, your immediate physical environment at home, work or school, the people around you, and your online environment should be adjusted to stimulate your brain away from old habits and towards the action that will create the habits you want to build instead. In this way, your environment can actually help to promote the necessary brain reprogramming to overcome the eating disorder.

The process to overcome an eating disorder is already difficult enough. Neural rewiring is challenging with any new learning, let alone when addictive habits are involved. Make it easier for yourself to get the results you need by making a few environmental changes, so that the things you see and hear each day and the people around you prompt you towards the thoughts and behaviours that you want.

Steps to Ensure Your Environment Supports Habit Change

- Fill your house with lots of calorie-dense and delicious food and remove restrictive *safe* foods.

- Put food by your bed so that if you wake in the night hungry you can reach for it or you can grab it first thing in the morning to help the day start positively and on an unrestricted path.

- Remove anything fitness related from your home. Give away or at the very least hide trainers, sports clothes and equipment that can otherwise trigger you automatically into engaging in habitual movement or exercise compulsions.

- Destroy or at least give away any scales. The scale debate is covered in Chapter 27 but if you want to abstain from weighing yourself then having scales in your home will make it harder. Kitchen scales and measuring devices should also go.

- Surround yourself with *normal* eaters whenever you can. If you don't have *normal* eaters at home then go and sit in coffee shops or somewhere else where people are naturally sitting, eating and relaxing. An added benefit to doing this is that social engagement also helps neuroplasticity!

- Put up notes or memes for yourself around your home and your digital world, such as your screensaver. Make them personal and meaningful to you so these constant reminders can motivate and reassure you when the inevitable anxiety or doubts set in about what you are doing.

- Create an inviting and cosy *nest* at home that can be a sacred and calming space to retreat to—somewhere you can relax and hunker down with food and perhaps a bit of Netflix (other streaming services are available).

- Clear your social media accounts so that you aren't following people who are diet or fitness influencers or who are triggering or disordered in their content. Instead either give up social media or follow genuine eating disorder recovery, body positivity or health at every size accounts. Or, just find some accounts with fluffy penguins to look at instead (much more fun I imagine and I'm sure penguins don't care about body weight or shape).

- Consider who you spend time with, not just online, but also in the real world. Being around people who are into dieting, exercise, body-building and those heavily influenced by diet culture will be hard when you are trying to move away from these messages to make the changes needed to overcome the eating disorder. If you really can't stop seeing those people then consider asking them not to talk about diet, exercise or weight loss topics in your presence. See Chapter 33 about diet talk.

- When you go food shopping, avoid the sections of the supermarket that have *diet products* or in which your usual *safe foods* are located. Instead frequent the sections that you usually avoid buying from and do just that.

Many more considerations could be added to this list. The key message is to spend time looking at what's in your environment–offline, online, inside and outside. Do a full environmental survey and make changes to ensure everything is set up to optimise your chances of triggering your brain away from old eating disorder habits and towards positive behaviours and foods that will enable you to develop the new habits you want.

Chapter 51

The Power of Self-Talk & Visualisation

The information covered so far about habit change and neuroplasticity to *reprogram* your brain has focused on actively changing your behaviours and thoughts. But your brain can begin to neurally rewire when you merely verbalise an intention, use self-talk or visualise the change.

When you have a conscious and focused thought about an action, your brain can relate it to the behaviour as if you are engaging in it and start to develop the relevant neural pathways. This is because you use the same neural networks to physically move as for thinking about moving. Therefore, repeatedly imagining a positive physical action with focus and intent, such as eating a big burger, can powerfully impact your brain reprogramming.

Of course, you can't overcome the eating disorder from thoughts and visualisation alone. Your brain isn't daft. It can tell the difference between whether or not you are actually doing something. But it will begin to build the pathways you want if you fully visualise the actions you want to take, applying positivity and determination.

Self-Talk is Powerful

Self-talk is very powerful. What you think and say to yourself and the things you visualise can impact how your brain changes, whether that self-talk is negative or positive. Self-talk will affect your beliefs and perceptions. Use it correctly and it can positively impact on your future free life.

Use self-talk in the direction of your desired future. Tell yourself that you are determinedly overcoming the eating disorder, that you will eat without restriction and rest like a sloth, imagining yourself doing these things as you say it. Doing so will begin to wire these concepts into your brain, increasing your self-confidence in your abilities and taking your current reality to new heights.

Talk To Yourself In The Third Person

Research has been conducted on self-talk and how to prevent constant self-chatter from sabotaging good intentions or elevating stress. One technique identified as beneficial in anxiety-provoking and stressful situations is something called *distanced self-talk*.

Distanced self-talk is said to be one of the fastest and most straightforward methods to gain perspective, calm yourself, increase self-control and reframe something that creates fear into a challenge[12]. The technique is simple. You talk to yourself in the second or third person. When you always think in the *I* pronoun, you stay focused on your negative inner voice. Change the pronoun to *you* or even use your name and it can positively impact your impulse control and interpretation of a situation.

Examples of this for overcoming an eating disorder might be to say to yourself,

> *You are going to eat the croissants with lots of Nutella and enjoy them.*

> *You are safe and comfortable. Just rest and relax.*

> *You will overcome this eating disorder, just keep going!*

Talk to yourself as you would talk to someone else and you can bestow more positivity and kindness on yourself.

When you are upset about something, you might also use your name in your self-talk. For example, I might say to myself,

> *Ok Helly, you are frustrated now but take a few minutes and then try again.*

Mental Rehearsal

Mental rehearsal with visualisation is another technique to adopt. Athletes, politicians and actors use mental rehearsal to improve their performance because it works. It can work in overcoming an eating disorder too.

Numerous research studies have been conducted into a range of subjects, including music performance, nursing skills and sports, repeatedly demonstrating that visual rehearsal can significantly improve the ability to perform. And it's not just motor skills this relates to but it helps with overcoming anxiety or other emotional reactions and the ability to develop a mental state that will support you when you are actually in the situation.

For mental rehearsal to work, you need to use your mind's eye to picture yourself doing whatever it is you want to accomplish, applying details and your full imagination. This will increase your awareness and the sense of expectation your brain has for the activity, while also changing and strengthening the relevant neural pathways.

To use this approach in overcoming the eating disorder, visualise situations that you know are anxiety-provoking. Make your imagined scenario as tough and detailed as you can as you visualise it. Progress through your visualised scenario, taking determined decisions and actions. The following steps will help produce optimal results:

1. Find a quiet space, deep breathe, close your eyes or soften your gaze and let your body relax.

2. Imagine the setting for the activity—where you are, what and who is there. Imagine the colours, sounds and smells.

3. Now, imagine you are a fly on the wall and watch yourself carrying out

the activity.

4. Then put yourself into the scene, engage in the activity, allow all your senses in, including positive emotions and keep going.

5. Slowly return to reality.

Repeat visualisations like this regularly and for a range of scenarios that you want to make possible. When you do then carry out these activities, your fear response will be not be as strong because your brain will perceive them as familiar and less of a threat.

Why Does Visualisation Work?

Visualisation works if the imagined experiences are as real as they can be by applying your senses and emotions. Your brain will then notice and commit them to memory in a similar way to actual events.

Anxiety usually rises in anticipation of an eating disorder-bashing activity but when you do it and your brain understands that you are still safe, your anxiety quickly drops back down. Using visualisation and mental rehearsal can trick your brain into recognising that the fear and anxiety it's generating to push you to avoid a situation isn't necessary, so you can proceed with more ease. Consider the situations you are avoiding, mentally rehearse them and then go tackle them head on!

1. Kross E, Bruehlman-Senecal E, Park J, Burson A, Dougherty A, Shablack H, Bremner R, Moser J, Ayduk O. Self-talk as a regulatory mechanism: how you do it matters. J Pers Soc Psychol. 2014;106(2):304-24. doi: 10.1037/a0035173. PMID: 24467424.

2. Gainsburg, I., & Kross, E. Distanced self-talk changes how people conceptualize the self. Journal of Experimental Social Psychology. 2020;88, Article 103969. https://doi.org/10.1016/j.jesp.2020.103969.

Chapter 52

Analyse Your Fear Response

O ne of the most powerful ways that a brain addicted to energy deficit will keep you locked into addictive habits is by generating fear-based responses. Some of the neuroscience underlying this is covered in *Addicted to Energy Deficit*. You will be more effective in managing your fear responses as you attempt to stop or change eating disorder-related habits or rituals when you can better understand them.

Your Brain Has Two Fear Pathways

Within your brain, two fear pathways can be triggered. The first is the one that you will be more familiar with—the instant, subconscious, fight-and-flight reaction. This is generated in the amygdala of your brain. When a threat is perceived, your amygdala instantly releases a surge of cortisol and adrenaline so your heart rate and blood pressure rise and your body gets prepared to respond, by fighting or fleeing.

The second pathway arises from the hippocampus in your brain. This is where explicit or conscious memories are stored, including painful or traumatic experiences which have been associated with a particular stimulus, such as a location or person. The fear response triggered by the hippocampus is slower and can take seconds or even minutes of processing.

The most common fear response that occurs with an eating disorder is the one arising from your amygdala. But it might be that you do have negative past experiences with food or perhaps from being bullied about your weight as a child, which are also now giving rise to fear or anxiety stemming from your hippocampus.

Fear as a Motivator

Fear isn't just a function of the brain to deter you from or prepare you to fight a particular threat, it can also be a strong motivator to drive you toward goals.

An example is a college student who has been slacking all year and not studying as hard as they should. As their final exams approach, the fear of failing is likely to be a strong motivator to push them into some serious cramming. This is a function of fear that you can harness in your efforts to overcome the eating disorder. Use the fear of what not overcoming the eating disorder will mean for your future as a strong motivator towards facing the difficult work to overcome it. The thought of staying in the cold, hollow, rigid, routine-driven and hungry world of an eating disorder for any longer than necessary should be a terrifying prospect. Regularly remind yourself what staying sick will mean and feel the fear that should come from that to spur you on when it feels impossible to keep going.

Become an Analyst of Your Fear

Become an analyst of any fear reactions that you have arising from the eating disorder. Stop and ask yourself, *What am I actually afraid of here?* Try to identify specifics.

If you can identify specifics, which might be gaining 10 lbs overnight, break it down further. *What am I afraid will happen if I did gain 10 lbs overnight?* Then do the same again and get to the root of the fear.

Analysing your fear response in this way can help you identify the true obstacles that are stopping you from making progress. When you can identify them, you can find new ways to proactively move forwards.

Rewiring a Fear Response

Reflect on a recent fear-based event that you have had with the eating disorder. What was it? What was your emotional reaction, what were your thoughts and self-talk in the moment and what deeper beliefs drove the reaction?

Now break this down further:

1. Identify the negative thought patterns that automatically came through when you had the fear response. Write them down. Then write down alternative thoughts to these—ones that are empowering and positive. Regularly repeat these new thoughts, allowing them to wire into your brain, perhaps forming them into affirmations (see Chapter 61). This will help to dampen future fear responses arising from your amygdala, giving your pre-frontal cortex time to apply a

more logical reaction.

2. Can you identify the core belief that was underlying the fear response you had? Identify the limiting belief and replace it with a new one. Ask, what evidence do I have that the old belief was false? Use that evidence to form a new belief and turn it into more positive thoughts so that you can wire these in as well.

3. Continuously change your actions and behaviours so that they reflect and support the new belief you want. This will help your brain to understand that this new belief is valid and should be wired in, while the original fear is no longer helpful.

So, in a nutshell, all you need to do is understand what triggered your fear reaction, analyse it, dig out the underlying thoughts and beliefs driving it and replace them with new ones... Simple right?!

I know all this sounds a bit therapy-ish and in many ways it is, but if you are struggling to make the changes you want to make because your fear response is too strong, then some deeper reflection on what's driving that fear might enable you to make more changes. Working with a therapist or coach on this can also help.

Chapter 53

Hack Your Physiology to Override a Fear Response

When a fear response has kicked in so you can feel your anxiety rising and your capacity for rational thought fading, threatening to jeopardise your eating disorder-bashing intentions, having some tools ready to implement to override the fear and proceed in a calmer state can be beneficial.

Let's imagine that you've decided to go to a restaurant with your family, order the most terrifying thing on the menu and eat every last morsel, no matter what. You feel determined, ready and committed. On the way there you can feel your anxiety rise but you remain focused and push away any thoughts trying to deter you. When you arrive and enter the restaurant, you are suddenly overcome with the conviction that this is wrong. Your brain is creating powerful and rational seeming reasons for why you need to leave and go home to eat the food you have there. You find yourself bolting for the exit, anger or irritability flaring at anyone who tries to stop you.

Does this sound familiar?

Perhaps you need to alter the scenario to one more relatable to you but I'm sure anyone who has an eating disorder can recognise the rapid and powerful fear response that can set in when you attempt to abstain from the eating disorder's habitual pursuit of energy deficit.

This is what happens when your rational and emotional brain regions conflict. Rationally you can decide to take a course of action that will be an excellent step to overcoming the eating disorder. This decision is made in your pre-frontal cortex, using reason and judgement. But in the moment, a fear response arises from your amygdala, hijacking your actions so that you flee or fight your way out of the situation, *almost* incapable of re-engaging rational thought.

So, what can you do when a fear response threatens to take over your actions to ensure you can go through with your intentions?

When you enter a fight-or-flight response, your brain triggers the release of powerful chemicals. Adrenaline and noradrenaline flood your brain and body, causing your heart and breathing rates to speed up and the blood to flow away from your skin surface and digestive system, towards your main muscle groups, preparing you to run. This leaves you feeling trembly, clammy and agitated. With this in mind, let's return to the restaurant scenario.

As you enter the restaurant and the fear is kicking in, it's likely you will feel your heart rate and breathing speed up and feel physically agitated, ready to flee the building. It's now that implementing some tools to hack your physiology could enable you to ride the fear and proceed in a calmer state.

Steps to Hack Your Physiology & Overcome a Fear Response

1. Just stop

Before anything else, when you notice the fear kicking in, just stop. There's no need to apply any thought—just stop. Then take a moment to try the following steps to adjust your physiology and shift your body out of the fear-based fight-and-flight mode into a calmer state and more rational frame of mind.

2. Adjust your visual field

When you are in a stressed or anxious state, as well as a rise in your heart rate and breathing, your visual field also changes. Your field of vision narrows and focuses on a single location, so you become less aware of all your surroundings and more focused solely on escape. To become calmer, stop and deliberately widen your field of vision. Imagine that your vision is in panoramic mode on your camera. If you can, look at the horizon and without moving your gaze bring to your attention what's on the sides, above and below you. This simple step can quickly help switch off your stress response.

3. Focus on your breathing, using *physiological sighs*

Yes, I know you have been told before to *breathe* when you are feeling stressed and anxious, but you might not know about this breathing hack. Physiological sighs are said to be one of the best tools available to rapidly calm yourself[1]. A physiological sigh is two quick inhalations through the nose followed by a slower exhalation through the mouth. Children who have been crying do this automatically as they reach a peak and start to calm down. A few deliberate physiological sighs are considered one of the fastest ways to return your body to *normal* from a stressed and anxious state. It's worth a try.

4. Relax your body and be still

When you enter a fear response and adrenaline is flying about your system, blood flows to the main muscles in your arms and legs, making you fidgety or shaky, with strong urges to move. Therefore, while also focusing on your vision and breathing, deliberately try to bring your body to stillness and relax your muscles. If you can, find somewhere to sit down and relax into the seat, being aware of the feel of the seat beneath you. Tell yourself you are safe. In doing so, your brain will understand that the need to escape or fight isn't valid because you aren't coming to any harm from the perceived threat despite being still. Your brain will then perceive it to be safe to switch off the fear response.

When you are in a situation in which a fear reaction is once again hijacking your excellent intentions, using these simple hacks could pull you out of fight-flight and not able to apply rational thought mode. Then, as you return to a calmer state, you can re-evaluate your situation, remember what you are doing and why, enabling you to proceed with renewed focus. And while you still have some adrenaline coursing through your veins, put it to good use and use the next tool in your fear-busting toolkit, which is to turn that fear into excitement!

---

1. https://youtu.be/rBdhqBGqiMc

Chapter 54

Turn Fear into Excitement

F ear can be real and powerful but what if you can turn it into excitement?

When you are working hard to overcome the eating disorder, facing more food each day and abstaining from other behaviours and rituals, failing to make progress can often result from some powerful fear responses. The last chapter provided a few tools to help manage fear and this chapter explains another effective technique worth trying.

What if I tell you that excitement, anxiety and fear are the same physiological reaction in your body? The differences between them relate to how your brain has conceptualised or interpreted the cause of the physiological changes.

As explained previously, during a fear response, you release adrenaline and cortisol in an instant surge preparing you to fight-or-flee danger. The limbic system in your brain takes over and blocks most rational thought so that you get tunnel vision, focused solely on escaping the threat. Your heart rate increases and you get jittery and sweaty. It's exactly the same reaction that occurs when you are excited.

If you are highly aroused with excitement, your brain and body are producing the same chemical reaction and response, only this time you don't feel scared, but you feel pumped up and hyper.

To clarify this, let's consider a lion and an antelope in the wild. The antelope sees a lion approach, ready to attack. It goes into a fear response, ready to run for its life, whereas the lion is excited and chasing the antelope. But the lion's physiology is just the same. Both animals have adrenaline pumping out, along with cortisol to keep their hearts beating faster and muscles moving. The antelope's brain is focused only on survival while the lion is focused on the excitement of the chase.

Therefore, if fear and excitement are physiologically the same, doesn't it beggar the question of whether we can turn inappropriate fear reactions encountered in the process of overcoming an eating disorder into excitement at facing the eating disorder head-on?

There were a few occasions when I unknowingly did just that. There were times in attempting to overcome the eating disorder that my anxiety was spiralling and I was trying to run from it. I wanted to use compulsive movement to ease it, while my brain focused on escaping unnecessary food intake. On these occasions, I managed to use inner frustration to flick the use of this intense physiological reaction from being in fight-or-flight mode to a positive and excited, attack mode. Instead of trying to escape, I became pumped up and forcefully charged at what I needed to do to address the eating disorder there and then. I grabbed the food that was terrorising me and used my tunnel vision to focus on my excitement about demolishing the food, not escaping it. And, it seems that this is not so ridiculous a notion. It's been demonstrated that it's easier for someone to turn high arousal from fear into an alternative highly aroused state than it is to calm down[1]. This is called anxiety reappraisal, which is to, *Stay aroused and get excited*.

Excitement and fear both stem from something unknown in the future but fear triggers us to escape it and excitement can move us towards it. So, can you reappraise each situation that generates fear as you overcome the eating disorder from one in which it is a threat into an exciting *opportunity*? Be excited and curious about approaching the situation head-on, rather than afraid, anxious and scared. Tell yourself when you feel your heart beating faster, your palms getting sweaty and your breath quickening, that this isn't fear, it's excitement. Your body is preparing you for attack and doing what it can to help you bash at the eating disorder, excitedly aiming for overshoot and a free life.

Next time you see a doughnut and want to run in terror, stay pumped up and use that adrenaline rush to approach and murder that doughnut and then bring on several more. When you do, you are likely to experience a rush of exhilaration, caused by a cocktail of feel-good brain chemicals making you feel incredible and believe it or not, you might find you want more of that great feeling and feel ready to take on another terrifying challenge immediately. If that urge hits, you owe it to your future self to keep going.

---

1. Hofmann SG, Heering S, Sawyer AT, Asnaani A. How to handle anxiety: The effects of reappraisal, acceptance, and suppression strategies on anxious arousal. Behav Res Ther. 2009 May; 47(5):389-94. doi: 10.10 16/j.brat.2009.02.010. Epub 2009 Feb 25. PMID: 19281966; PMCID: PMC2674518.

Chapter 55

The Maybe Tool

The coming chapters provide some more generally practical and helpful tools to use as you ride the challenging rollercoaster of overcoming an eating disorder and finding your free life. The first is the *Maybe* tool which helps to manage eating disorder-generated anxiety-based thoughts.

It's likely that anxiety-based thoughts and predictions have become habitual patterns of thinking and powerful triggers to you engaging in eating disorder behaviours.

A restrictive eating disorder creates thoughts that will taunt you—perhaps telling you that you will find gaining weight impossible to cope with—triggering you to continue to eat restrictively and engage in compensatory behaviours to prevent the feared weight gain. In practice, this can manifest as a thought of, *If I gain weight, everyone will think I've let myself go*, triggering you to put on your shoes and go for a long walk, rather than sit down to eat a doughnut.

When you recognise these thoughts are generated by your addiction to energy deficit and that they arise from your brain securing the dopamine fix it craves, you can address them. These thoughts are frequent and habitual because, over time, your brain has learnt that creating these thoughts works. If you feel anxious about gaining weight, you engage in energy deficit-creating behaviours, which is what your brain wants. The way out of this loop is to teach your brain that these thoughts and the associated anxiety are no longer going to have the same results. Techniques to manage the thoughts so that they don't trigger you into eating-disordered behaviours are critical and will enable you to take your control back.

When you are consumed by the eating disorder, you live with a safe sense of certainty that if you continue to eat x foods and engage in the same habitual behaviours each day, you will maintain the level of energy deficit your brain is addicted to, enabling you to feel less anxious and more *normal*. Your brain tells you that you won't cope with gaining weight and attaches emotion and convincing stories to this. These stories might include that weight gain will make you less loveable, memories of being bullied for being fat in the past or concerns about losing your level of *fitness*. These thoughts keep you stuck.

Understandably, this uncertainty impacts you. Your brain is hard-wired to dislike any uncertainty and if it can't confidently predict an outcome, the survival response is to fear the worse (better safe than sorry). Therefore, uncertainty is naturally stressful. In fact, uncertainty about a stressful situation is even more stressful than if the feared situation does occur. For example, people told that they **will** experience pain after an operation are usually calmer than those told they **might** experience pain and left in uncertainty about it.

Unfortunately, no one can tell you with any certainty what will come in relation to the things you feel anxious and uncertain about with overcoming the eating disorder. For example, no one can give you certainty with what size or shape your unsuppressed body will settle at, when your hunger will normalise or what your self-identity will be when you are free of the eating disorder. You are going to need to be able to sit with uncertainty with all of this and more, accepting it for what it is.

The *Maybe* tool can help you to manage any uncertain scenario. When you use it, you choose to accept a level of uncertainty about what will be. When you can answer anxiety-driven thoughts with a, *Maybe that will happen but maybe it won't,* allowing the uncertainty, you can start to move beyond it.

Acknowledge that your feared outcome is possible with a, *Maybe it will happen.* Meet the taunting weight gain thoughts with a, *Maybe I will blow up to the size of a house and keep gaining weight for the rest of my days.* When you do this, you stop the eating disorder from successfully taunting you into mind games that can otherwise suck you into a spiral of negative thoughts.

Saying, *Anything is possible,* is confirming that the circumstances your brain wants you to fear could happen but equally they might not. When you do this, you are back in the driver's seat.

More examples of how to use the *Maybe* tool are:

Thought - *You could gain weight forever. The weight gain will never stop once it starts.*
Your response - *Sure, anything is possible.*

Thought - *If you eat that cake now, you will regret it and then have to restrict and exercise later.*
You - *Maybe that's so, or maybe I will feel good and have another slice.*

Thought - *If you don't have an eating disorder anymore then you won't know who you are and life will be intolerable.*
You - *This could happen. We will see.*

The responses you give when you use the *Maybe* tool need to be final and determined. Your response of, *Maybe it will happen but maybe it won't,* needs to shut down any further internal dialogue.

These responses take practice. It means noticing the thoughts when they arise and shutting them down before you more deeply engage with them. In this way, the *Maybe* tool can stop you from getting into loops of overthinking and going down the rabbit hole of increasingly disastrous thoughts which stop you from making progress to overcome the eating disorder.

Remove the power from the anxiety-provoking thoughts and stories your brain is creating. Stay focused on aiming for overshoot and just see if maybe you do want to keep eating thousands and thousands of calories a day forever—or maybe you won't.

Chapter 56
Chase Fear & Face Triggers

O vercoming an eating disorder involves taking control back from all the ways in which your brain keeps you stuck in compulsively habitual thought pathways and automatic behaviours.

Anxiety and fear are emotions designed to make us move away from whatever is generating them. Fear is an evolutionary survival response to a perceived threat and needs to be a forceful drive to find safety.

Triggers can be anything that make eating disordered thoughts and urges worse. They will push you back into eating disordered behaviours before you realise what's happened. It's important to identify your particular triggers as you overcome the eating disorder but the usual advice is to avoid them.

When you take control back from the eating disorder and your brain's addictive patterns, it can be empowering to chase the fear, rather than run from it and deliberately expose yourself to triggers, rather than avoid them. In doing so, you change your automatic reactions to situations, allowing your brain to wire in new responses to your fears and triggers.

Chase the Fear

When your brain develops an addiction, it will use fear and anxiety, arising from your amygdala, to deter you from anything that might stop it from getting a hit of the *drug* it's addicted to. With a restrictive eating disorder, your drug is energy deficit and so you are likely to experience anxiety or even a full-blown fear response to anything that could lead to weight gain, which requires energy surplus.

Eating beyond habitual restrictive amounts that feel *safe* becomes terrifying, not engaging in compensatory behaviours creates distress and anxiety, and the thought of weight gain can be intolerable. These are very real fear reactions your brain is creating and they hold immense power in driving your behaviours, often before you have become consciously aware of what's happening.

However, when you can identify how and when fear and anxiety arise for you and the effect they have on tripping you up in your efforts to overcome the eating disorder, you can address it.

This is where the tool of chasing fear is valuable.

An example of chasing fear is that you hate the thought of gaining weight, let alone overshoot. The thought of gaining weight beyond your set point feels terrifying as just gaining to your set point is frightening enough. These thoughts and fears are created by a restrictive eating disorder that's keeping you stuck. Instead of allowing these thoughts and this perceived fear of weight gain to stop you from making progress, chase the fear. As the title of this book suggests, chase overshoot with determination, even a glimmer of glee. Do it despite the fear. Even force yourself to laugh at the fear. Laugh at the fact that you are scared of being in a bigger body and that your brain is trying to keep you in a suboptimal state and deliberately push ahead. Eat all the foods your brain creates a fear reaction to, deliberately hunting them down and tackling them. Decide you will rest on the couch all day long and not compensate for all the bowls of cheesy and creamy pasta you have enjoyed today. Let your body gain weight and choose to welcome those gains as the incredible wins they are. Deliberately push forwards so that all the eating-disordered thoughts, fears and anxieties leave you free to live a bigger and fuller life.

Face the Triggers

Triggers can be incredibly powerful at pushing you back into eating disordered thoughts and behaviours before you realise what's happened. And triggers can be absolutely anything from a certain time of day, a location, a person, something that has been said, a change in a physical sensation, an emotional state, a memory, the weather or any one of a million other things. You will have a vast number of triggers that affect you every day and lead your brain down automatic eating disordered paths without you realising it. As I said above, in the process of overcoming the eating disorder, it's important to identify as many of your triggers as you can, which will be an ongoing task because so many are insidious.

When you first identify your triggers, you will want to eliminate as many of them as possible or actively avoid them. There will be many triggers you can't avoid though and those that, no matter how much you try to avoid, you will have to face eventually. Therefore, carefully and deliberately exposing yourself to known triggers is beneficial as you make progress to overcome the eating disorder.

Deliberately exposing yourself to the triggers that pull you back into compulsive habits enables you to find new ways to respond to them and in this way is a powerful approach. Triggers are most dangerous when you meet with them unexpectedly and they trigger an automatic response before you know what's happened. But when you deliberately approach your triggers and change your response, you teach your brain new ways of reacting which will ultimately become wired into the new circuits your brain is building. An example of this might be that you decide to meet with a friend who you know is going to comment on how much and what you are eating but you choose to do so with a determined, *Whatever they say today will not trigger me back and I will keep eating, resting and allowing myself to escape energy deficit no matter what.* This is when you claim your power back from past triggers and consciously choose your own *Feck it-style* approach to your future.

Chapter 57

If-Then Planning

Because of how decisively determined you are on overcoming the eating disorder, I'm sure that you have taken the information from this book and perhaps from *Addicted to Energy Deficit* and made yourself some clear eating disorder-bashing commitments. They might even be similar to:

- I will abstain from all restrictive eating.

- I will abstain from all unnecessary movement (formal exercise and lower-level movement).

- I will abstain from all purging behaviours.

- I will avoid doing anything else to manipulate my body weight or shape.

- I will joyfully aim for overshoot!

That all sounds incredible, doesn't it?

Commitments like these are an excellent way to put your intentions in black and white for yourself and anyone you wish to share them with. They decisively say, *This is what I'm doing to overcome this eating disorder.*

Let's now come back to reality for a moment. It's easy to make these commitments, fully intending to keep to them, but then find that it isn't happening. This isn't surprising when your intentions are so broad. Happily, a tool called, *If-Then planning*, can help you to take your superb commitments to another level.

The Gap Between Knowing Your Commitments & Achieving Them

There's very often a big gap between knowing what you want to do to overcome the eating disorder and doing it. It's all too easy for distractions, procrastination, strong existing habits and powerful emotional reactions to side-track you from your excellent intentions.

Therefore, it's important to find ways to ensure you take consistent action, even when obstacles try to hijack you. This is where *If-Then* statements come in.

If-Then statements are very simple. It's as simple as, *If x happens, Then I will do y*.

These simple plans take your commitments out of the clouds and pin them down to concrete moments or situations in your daily life.

If-Then Plans Work

If-Then planning is used for all aspects of life when people want to change their habits, their lifestyle or achieve hard-to-reach goals. Research into these simple statements shows that you are two to three times more likely to succeed at sticking to your intentions if you use an If-Then plan than if you don't[1].

When you are aiming for goals related to something as difficult to achieve as overcoming an eating disorder, it's worth implementing anything you can to make sticking to your commitments easier.

Why If-Then Plans Work

On a brain-based level, if you can pin your commitments down and tie them to specific triggers or situations, such as, *If I'm thinking about food, then I have to eat the densest and scariest thing I can find*, the lack of choice makes it easier to form the rewiring you want because you have already chosen your path.

If-Then statements can remove anxiety-provoking indecision and instead help you to maintain focus and nail down stronger commitments. This then forces the neural connections that you need to build for brain circuitry that isn't driven by an eating disorder into being.

If-Then statements ultimately speak your brain's language.

Your brain enjoys contingency patterns, *If x, Then y*, and frequently uses this process, on an unconscious level, to guide your behaviours and instantaneous decisions. When you make your own intentional If-Then plans, you are encouraging your brain into a pattern it understands but in a new direction of your choice.

Link If-Then Plans To Daily Cues

Cues and triggers are things that your brain recognises and lead you to take habitual paths without conscious awareness. And as explained before, these cues can be a certain time of day, a pattern of behaviours that cue you to take the next behaviour, specific automatic thoughts or something in your environment.

Commitments will be more successfully achieved when you relate them to a cue. Decide exactly where and when you will act on your commitments and you ultimately create a link in your brain between the situation or cue (the If) and the action that will follow (the Then).

Examples of this are:

If it's morning and my eyes are open, then I find food and eat it.

If I'm thinking about going for a walk or run, then I'll grab snacks, sit on the couch and message a friend for support.

If I'm comparing my portion size to someone else's, then I'll deliberately get double the portion they are eating.

If I'm body checking, with negative thoughts about my body, then I'll immediately lovingly rub the area I'm criticising and think positive thoughts about it instead, visualising the future I'm working towards, knowing a bigger body will help reach it.

Let's consider the first of these examples more closely. The cue of it being morning and you being awake will start to become wired into your brain directly to the action, I find and eat food. Now the situation of waking up in the morning becomes something of greater significance to your brain, and subconsciously, your brain will start scanning your environment for the *if* part of your plans. When it recognises the *if* part is happening, it will try to activate the t*hen* part, so that this becomes your new automatic response. This means that even if you are more distracted than usual, you are more likely to still achieve your original commitment.

In this way, If-Then plans need less conscious effort, mental energy or willpower than you need for a written commitment alone.

If-Then Plans For Unexpected Events

The above use of If-Then planning relates to linking the cues to things that you might encounter every day in your general life. However, If-Then statements can also be used for unexpected situations, in which you still want to maintain your commitments through your actions.

For this, you need to consider situations that might not happen but that you want to be prepared for. Having these statements prepared and rehearsed before you encounter them will prevent you from becoming tripped up by these potential future events.

Lay out ground rules for yourself with If-Then plans by thinking about different situations before they occur and it removes the need to make difficult decisions in a potentially very stressful situation.

Examples here might be:

If I'm in a restaurant, looking at the menu and undecided, then I'll let the waiter decide for me.

If a friend invites me out for lunch, then I'll say yes immediately and order the scariest option, no matter what they are choosing.

If I get stuck when I'm out and can't get home to eat, then I'll go into the nearest fast-food restaurant for a full meal deal.

Get detailed and plan for all types of triggers and situations you can think of.

In doing this, you will remove your ability to make excuses for not following through on your commitments and it will strengthen your ability to keep to them.

Put If-Then Planning Into Practice

To put If-Then planning into practice, you will need to take some time to think about them in detail. Your If-Then plans need to be meaningful for you and relevant to your situations and circumstances. Reflect on what points in your day you are more likely to get pulled off course in your process. Where do you most need contingency plans?

Set yourself up several If-Then statements for all sorts of cues (Ifs) and the recovery positive action you want to follow those cues with (Thens).

Write out your statements that are relevant to your life. Re-read them. Share them with others. Stick them on the wall or somewhere you can refer back to them regularly so that your brain builds that link between the If... cue and what it needs to guide you to do next when it recognises the cue is present.

And ultimately, commit to your statements. Don't question them when the time comes, just follow them, knowing this is right for you.

If-Then planning can help take the process you are working through to overcome the eating disorder from a hard, frustrating and painstaking slog to being just a little bit easier.

---

1. Bieleke M, Keller L, & Gollwitzer PM. If-then planning. European Review of Social Psychology. 2021;32(1), 88–122. https://doi.org/10.1080/10463283.2020.1808936.

Chapter 58

The Pre-Mortem Tool

You already know what a post-mortem is—a process carried out after a disastrous situation has occurred, evaluating the events in minute detail to establish what went wrong, how and why, to learn lessons from them. A post-mortem after any disaster is an essential and valuable exercise.

But should we wait for disaster to strike before we consider what might go wrong in a particular scenario? It makes sense to evaluate a given situation and put measures in place to minimise the risk of disaster arising. And this is exactly what you do when you carry out a pre-mortem.

You are probably wondering what this has to do with overcoming an eating disorder. Well, a pre-mortem can be a beneficial tool when you take the time to implement one.

What's the Role of a Pre-Mortem as You Overcome an Eating Disorder?

Overcoming an eating disorder necessitates putting yourself in frequent stressful situations, often multiple times a day. And it's likely that when these stressful situations are unexpected and so you are unprepared, the results won't be as you would have hoped.

When your brain is under stress, it releases cortisol and adrenaline and your body shuts down non-essential functions, like digestion, the immune system and the ability to feel emotions other than fear. Your brain becomes cloudy and foggy so you lose the ability to think clearly and rationally, making your ability to systematically deal with the stressful situation much harder.

This is why you can have the best of intentions when you are in a calm and rational frame of mind to charge at the eating disorder and bash it hard but find that when it comes to putting those intentions into action, your stress response kicks in and takes over. This is because your brain wants to hold onto the rewards created by behaviours that lead to or maintain energy deficit and will create a stress response to deter you from anything that might take you away from it. In this stressed state, your ability for rational thought disappears and your best intentions are forgotten. You instead find that you can't think clearly or remember why you were ever planning to eat or rest more. Suddenly you have resorted back to old habits and the restriction that your brain mistakenly perceives as safe.

You might now be starting to see the potential benefit of a pre-mortem tool to minimise the risk of *disaster* when you are in a stressful, eating disorder-related situation. Regular pre-mortems can help you to manage the all too common and frustrating scenario in which your stressed brain stalls your hard efforts to beat the eating disorder.

How to Carry Out a Pre-Mortem

With a pre-mortem, you look towards an upcoming situation and imagine you have a crystal ball to gaze into where you know that the event in question has gone badly. Then you use all the imagined disastrous scenarios to establish what you can do before the event to prevent those things from happening or at least apply damage limitation.

By doing this exercise you are acknowledging that when you are in the situation you are likely to be under a high level of stress and less able to apply the clarity of thought you would have liked. Your results from the pre-mortem should enable you to put systems in place for when you really are in the situation to ensure that things go better than they otherwise might have done, even if you are in an anxious and less rational state of mind at the time.

Hopefully, this is all making sense, but let's apply it to a typical scenario that you will very possibly face as you overcome the eating disorder.

Applying a Pre-Mortem to a Typical Eating Disorder-Bashing Situation

Imagine that you have a family party coming up. It's going to be a sit-down meal with lots of family members. You haven't been to such a gathering for years because of the eating disorder but this time you know that you are in the process of overcoming it and you can't keep avoiding situations like this. You are determined to go, join in, eat the delicious foods and then sit and relax with your loved ones for the rest of the day.

In an ideal world, this plan alone would be enough to ensure that the situation described is actually what happens, but let's not forget one little detail. You do still have an eating disorder. Even though you are making great efforts in your process to overcome it, big family meals are not something you are comfortable with yet. Therefore, in reality, it's likely to make your brain a bit stressed when you are there.

Now, if you apply the pre-mortem exercise before you go, you will use your crystal ball and imagine all the possible ways in which things could go badly on the day:

- Aunty Mildred comments that, *you are looking a little plump and are you sure you do want that many roast potatoes;*

- you take one look at the feast laid out and your brain goes into such a spasm and panic that you find yourself making an excuse for why you have to leave. You are bolting for the door before anyone can stop you or you can stop yourself;

- you find yourself making excuses to be away from any situation that involves sitting and eating, so you are the one being *helpful* with bringing dishes in and out, washing up and tidying. You get through the meal-time without eating much at all;

- you get through the meal but then you volunteer to take the dog for a long *innocent* walk afterwards, which is the result of an ongoing exercise compulsion and urge to compensate for the food you have eaten.

If you were to carry out your pre-mortem of such a scenario, the predicted ways in which things could go wrong will be unique to you, what you know about yourself and how the eating disorder manifests. Everyone with an eating disorder is unique so if some of these scenarios are things you can't relate to, it doesn't invalidate your experience with an eating disorder or the strength of it.

Once you have considered all the possible ways that things might go wrong in the upcoming situation, you can take each one and consider what you can do to minimise the risk of it occurring or plan how to deal with it if it does.

Apply pre-mortems to all types of situations and eventualities. It might be that plans change at the last minute for something, things happen outside your control or influence or other people are less reliable than you hoped and not present to provide support. Use a pre-mortem to come up with ways you can adapt and react in any situation so that you can roll with the punches and stay on top.

Pre-mortems can be equally applied to things on a wide scale in the process of overcoming the eating disorder as much smaller situations.

You might decide to take a broad view and carry out a pre-mortem of what might jeopardise your whole process or it might be something much more detailed and specific, such as pushing yourself to start eating much earlier in the day than you usually would.

Use the crystal ball method for whatever the situation is and look at it with the certain knowledge that the outcome has been a fiasco.

Imagine all the ways in which things could go wrong and list them. If you have an eating disorder-support person then they could do this with you and use their insight to come up with some additional ideas.

Use the Pre-Mortem to Prevent & Manage any *Disasters*

Going through the above exercise will help to raise your awareness as to what might hold you back from getting the results you want in a particular situation so that if these things do happen, your brain will be more likely to recognise them.

But by taking the pre-mortem process a step further and establishing steps you can take to minimise the risk of each predicted outcome from happening, you can effectively apply damage control.

The last chapter covered *If-Then* planning. Now it's time in your pre-mortem to combine your crystal ball scenarios with some If-Then plans.

As explained with If-Then planning, when your brain has predicted a situation ahead of time and that situation occurs, your brain will be more likely to recognise it and remember, *I had a plan for this,* rather than brain fog and fight-or-flight mode setting in. Therefore, let's return to our imagined family party and some of the predicted ways in which it might not go as hoped.

You might plan ahead of time exactly what you will say if anyone does comment on your recent weight changes or on how much you are eating. So, you might plan to respond with a proud, *Thank you, yes I have gained weight because I've been overcoming a devastating eating disorder and I'm proud of my new curves and most definitely will have more potatoes.*

If you do find yourself tempted to charge out the door rather than stay at the party because the fear response has taken over, then you might tell yourself that you predicted this could happen but that you do want to stay and enjoy this day. Remind yourself that you are determined to stay focused on beating the eating disorder which means that you will darn well eat the food, sit and enjoy the company and not let this eating disorder ruin another opportunity to be with loved ones. You might also plan to have someone there who is a support to you for the day and who you can turn to when needed.

Try It!

Using regular pre-mortems in the process to overcome the eating disorder can help you achieve overall success a little faster and with more ease than you would otherwise. They can stop you from facing ongoing frustration that another *challenge* failed or that another day has been *wasted* because you didn't manage to do what you wanted.

Give it a go. It might just work. And if you do carry out a pre-mortem and situations still go wrong (which they inevitably will because overcoming an eating disorder is never linear), then there's still the good old post-mortem exercise to perform to ensure things do go better next time.

Chapter 59

Radical Acceptance

If you have ever had psychotherapy, you might be familiar with radical acceptance. Radical acceptance is a useful tool as you overcome the eating disorder and you don't need to work with a therapist to use it. You can either apply it yourself or talk it through with a coach, a trusted friend or family member.

Radical acceptance can help you to accept your emotions and apply cognitive reappraisal to a situation, turning a negative take on it into a positive one[1].

As the name suggests, radical acceptance involves accepting what is and avoiding judgment, no matter how challenging that is. With a restrictive eating disorder, you will often try to escape your reality. Whether that's by fighting your natural body size and shape, numbing your true emotions through addictive behaviours, suppressing your authentic self or running from fear or anxiety. All these things prevent you from accepting your present and facing painful emotions, while simultaneously holding you in patterns of attempting to control things through destructive behaviours.

Radical acceptance can be applied to all kinds of things in life that are hard or where you want to change. With an eating disorder, examples of practising radical acceptance might be saying to yourself,

I don't like that I can't control my body size or predict how big it will be at my set point but I'll accept it for the mental freedom it brings me; or

Eating this meal feels wrong and it's making me anxious but I can sit with this discomfort.

When you first practise radical acceptance, apply it to a particular situation or emotional state. Let's use the example of having ordered a pasta meal in a cafe for lunch and when it arrives it's much bigger and cheesier than you anticipated. You are feeling anxious and thoughts are flying in about how much weight it will make you gain and if you eat it, whether you should restrict later or find other ways to compensate. You are feeling distracted and agitated. If you were to apply radical acceptance in this situation, you would take the following steps:

- **Acknowledge the situation and observe your reaction**

Take a deep breath, acknowledge that you are anxious about the meal and that you are questioning the situation. Let go of any *should haves* or *could haves.* If you have thoughts that, *I could have ordered the salad,* or, *I should have stayed at home for lunch,* then recognise these as hypothetical and not your current reality. Remind yourself that your reality is as it is and you can manage it.

- **The past has gone and we cannot predict the future**

When thoughts come about what you should have done earlier that day to avoid this situation now or the impact that eating this lunch will have on your urges to compensate or on your weight, just acknowledge that you can't change the past and can't predict what the future will be. All you have is this moment and you can choose how to respond to it.

- **Use acceptance techniques**

Use techniques to help you accept the current situation. This will enable you to relax. Remind yourself of what you want from your future when you are free of the eating disorder. Use any mental images you have of that free life—a life where eating out is a relaxing event, no matter what food is presented. Adopt breathing techniques to help you relax or choose to turn the fear reaction into one of excitement instead. Positive self-talk and mantras that enable you to accept the current situation can also be beneficial.

- **Consider what you would do if you were to accept this reality for what it is**

Identify what you would do if you did accept this reality for what it is, recognising its place in your process to overcome the eating disorder. Detaching yourself from your emotional response, consider the steps you would take if you were to accept this meal and the situation. Then take that action. This is similar to a *fake it to make it* approach and it can work.

- **Release any judgments of yourself or others and apply self-compassion**

Consider the situation from a non-judgmental perspective. Once again, remove emotion from the equation. Don't judge yourself for your choices, your reaction, the things that led to this situation or what might arise from it and don't judge others either. We are all only human.

- **Allow yourself to feel disappointed, frustrated or sad**

The fact that this situation occurred and you reacted the way you did might leave you feeling disappointed or frustrated. Allow yourself to feel these things—don't try to block the emotions—and let yourself process them.

- **Learn from the situation and move on**

Reflect on the event and your response to it afterwards. Without judgment or self-criticism, consider how your reaction made you feel and what you could do differently next time.

Radical acceptance can be a positive tool that will enable you to stop yourself from pushing back against a situation, past event or uncertain future and allow things to be as they are. This in turn can reduce any anxiety or frustration you have and enable a sense of calm. When you can recognise that you can't change the past or predict the future and that life won't always be as you like but that's ok, then you can accept and deal with the things you need to face in the now.

Repeating mantras to yourself is another great way to radically accept your current reality. Examples of helpful mantras include:

It is what it is;

So it goes;

This is how it has to be;

I'm strong and I'll survive this, and

I can't predict the future.

Feck it—I'm aiming for overshoot and anything goes!!

1. Segal O, Sher H, Aderka I & Weinbach N. Does acceptance lead to change? Training in radical acceptance improves implementation of cognitive reappraisal. Behaviour Research and Therapy. 2023;104303. 10.1016/j.brat.2023.104303.

Chapter 60

Swearing Really Can Help

Although I'm not encouraging anyone to become potty-mouthed in all aspects of their lives, offending children, older people and polite society, I do believe that when overcoming an eating disorder, the power of a little well-placed cursing shouldn't be underestimated. If you have been suppressing your emotions and numbing yourself by using eating disorder behaviours for a long time, swearing might be cathartic and help you release, rather than numb, some of the inevitable emotions that arise.

The main language centres of your brain are located in the left hemisphere—in the Broca's and the Wernicke's areas. But spontaneous swearing comes from a different brain region. It arises from the emotional part of your brain—the amygdala and limbic system. This is where your fight-or-flight response centre is located and for this reason, it's thought that swearing is the brain's response to a perceived threat[1]. This has been likened to when other animals cry out, shriek or growl if they are startled or feel threatened. Swearing can be a basic, evolutionary means to express frustration, passion, anger or fear.

Swearing can help you to reduce your inhibitions, take off the mask you wear daily and dig deeper into your core feelings and emotions. It's a powerful method to intensify the expression of your emotions, which is something you might have struggled with since having an eating disorder. It can help you to act on your authentic feelings and intentions with more urgency and make those intentions real. And it's not just negative emotions that can be expressed through swearing—highly positive ones can too—such as exhilaration, excitement, anticipation and joy.

Other benefits of swearing include its ability to increase attention and recall, stimulate physiological responses, release endorphins, promote stamina and strength and reduce pain. Emotional pain is known to be felt in a very similar way to physical pain, so the pain-relieving effects of swearing are likely to have positive effects on both pain types.

You can probably now appreciate why swearing as you overcome an eating disorder can have benefits. At times, you need to be in fight mode to overcome those urges pulling you towards restriction or energy deficit and to spur you to take action in the opposite direction. You need to stop using eating disorder behaviours to suppress your emotions and so any tools that help to manage the resulting emotional pain are going to be welcome.

But of course, swearing does need some censorship. When you are with others who aren't familiar with you or your situation, swearing can be deemed to be aggressive, even if it isn't directed at anyone else.

It's also important to note that the above benefits of swearing are based on *cathartic* swearing. This is when swearing is largely automatic and reflexive. This differs from *social* swearing which is consciously applied in conversation and doesn't share the same benefits.

So don't be afraid of the odd expletive erupting from your core as you overcome the eating disorder and start to feel the resulting emotions, whether they are frustration, anger, sadness and fear, or excitement, exhilaration and joy.

Swearing definitely had a place when I was addressing the eating disorder and beginning to release the emotional tension I'd kept suppressed for so long. In fact, swearing had such an impact on me that I wrote a blog post about it at the time, from which this is an extract:

> *Does anyone else find that they go through life rarely swearing but when it comes to anything to do with an eating disorder their language becomes less than polite? Maybe it's just me... but I don't think so.*

> *I've recently turned into a person who can curse with the best of them. If I had to pay a penny for every time I have sworn since starting this recovery—well my debt would be well beyond the means of even Richard Branson.*

> *But you know what? Sometimes swearing helps.*

> *Applying an expletive to this cruel eating disorder can make me feel better and recently, very little achieves that.*

> *Sometimes I might swear at the eating disorder or at what it's doing to me or I might swear for the sake of letting off some inner frustration. Sometimes I swear to shake myself into action..... "Just eat the f**king food", is a bit of therapeutic self-talk I've successfully deployed lately and without the F-word in there, it doesn't have the same effect.*

> *Apparently, a swear word in a sentence can make us more persuasive, shocking our listeners (who could just be ourselves) into understanding the emotional force behind the words. So, yes, I*

think swearing is a big help at times, even if it's not always socially acceptable!

Extract from a blog post written for RecoveringNomad.com;

2019

Don't be afraid of a little swearing as you overcome the eating disorder. Use it to let the emotions out. Let's face it, science proves that swearing can be therapeutic and who are we to argue with science?

---

1. Stapleton K, Beers Fägersten K, Stephens R & Loveday C. The power of swearing: What we know and what we don't. Lingua. 2022;277. https://doi.org/10.1016/j.lingua.2022.103406.

Chapter 61

Affirmations

Self-affirmations can positively impact your ability to overcome an eating disorder. They need to be used correctly and be meaningful to you but when this is the case, they can support your brain's reprogramming and help you change your behaviours.

Everyone has constant internal dialogue whenever they are awake. Depending on the nature of this dialogue, it can motivate you or hold you back, increase your anxiety or stress or even be bullying. If you are constantly worrying about not making progress with overcoming the eating disorder, all the things you have missed out on in life and fears about what's happening tomorrow, you can become exhausted and depressed and it will impact on your progress. It is here that positive affirmations can help to shift your internal thoughts from constant negative chatter to something more positive.

Research into the value of self-affirmations demonstrates their potential benefits across a variety of challenging situations[1]. These benefits include helping to release stress, counter-acting negative thoughts, increasing your well-being, improving academic performance and, very importantly, they can help with behaviour change. Self-affirmations can remind you of your positive self-worth and values beyond a perceived threat or stressful situation. This then reduces your automatic reaction to the threat and helps to protect your emotional well-being.

Affirmations increase activity in your brain regions for reward and positive valuation, particularly when the affirmations are future-focused. In this way, self-affirmations can improve your self-worth and help you reflect on your core values. They can help you develop a more optimistic way of looking at yourself, your experiences and your future.

Interestingly, cognitive biases can also shift through the use of affirmations. Cognitive biases are the way your brain scans your environment for evidence that the things it believes to be true are valid, ignoring evidence to the contrary. Therefore, your cognitive biases might make you very susceptible to noticing diet culture messages above those that conflict with them. With positive affirmations, you can start to teach your brain a new way to perceive the world and your view of your place in it. As a result, your brain will start to subconsciously search for signs that confirm these new views you are teaching it, bringing these to your conscious attention. This means that you notice more evidence in your world that support you in moving towards your goals, reassuring you that it's the right thing to do.

Ego fatigue is a concept covered in *Addicted to Energy Deficit*. This is when you become mentally drained by having to keep saying no to yourself and continuous eating disorder impulses. Ego fatigue can be a significant risk to whether you succeed in abstaining from the behaviours or not. Self-affirmations can increase your mental strength and ability to deal with impulses or stressful situations and so help with ego fatigue.

Affirmations also help with neuroplasticity (your brain's ability to rewire and reprogram). Just as visualisation can help your brain to learn new things, repeating affirming statements about yourself can encourage your brain to take these affirmations as facts. When you have a greater belief you can do something, it's more likely the actions to support this belief will be easier to pursue.

To gain these benefits from self-affirmations, you need to use them correctly. Repeating a few sentences to yourself, without focusing, applying emotions to them or while telling yourself that the statements aren't true, won't make a jot of difference. You can't mindlessly and numbly repeat words that you believe are lies and expect your brain or behaviours to change.

For some people, affirmations won't work because they can't even begin to believe the things they are trying to tell themselves or visualise the reality of the statements. When this is the case, affirmations can lead to internal conflict and elevated stress because you are trying to repeat statements to yourself that are the polar opposite of your core beliefs. If you have long-standing negative beliefs based on feelings of shame and very low self-worth, which have roots in past trauma or memories, then it's advisable to do more work to address this first with a therapist.

That's not to say though that you have to wholeheartedly believe all your affirmation statements when you start practising them. Not at all. You just need some level of belief that they can be true for you now or in your future and to feel the positive emotions that can sit alongside them.

How To Practise Self-Affirmations

For affirmations to be most effective, make them part of your routine so they become a positive habit. Try to set aside a few minutes a day, ideally at the same time each day, such as before brushing your teeth in the morning and at night, to repeat the affirmations to yourself.

Repeat each one, ideally out loud and with pride, about ten times and focus on the words and their meaning, believing them to be true. Allow yourself to feel positive emotions while you do so.

When writing your affirmations they should be specific, in the present tense and future-focused. Using *I* within them, choose positive, optimistic statements that resonate with you and link to your core values. Ideally write your own, although you can use those created by others, as long as they are meaningful to you.

Examples of Affirmations for Someone Overcoming an Eating Disorder:

- I can overcome this eating disorder and have a free life.

- I can say no to others when it means I say yes to my needs.

- I can accept my growing body and appreciate it at any size.

- I can enjoy resting and relaxing, allowing my body to restore and heal.

- I can eat what I want, when I want and not let anything stop me.

- I am proud of who I am and to own my place in this world.

- I can be body-positive and proud, setting a positive example to my children and others around me (this one would speak to your values of not wanting to be a victim of diet culture).

And, my personal self-affirmation statement:

- I am an eating disorder-bashing superhero. I can eat freely, rest happily and be proud of my curves!

Self-affirmations hold real potential value in your process to beat the eating disorder. Make them meaningful to you and practice them each day. At first, it might feel weird, clunky and wrong but keep at it and be patient. Brain changes happen over time with repetition so keep practising while also persisting with the other work you need to do to address the eating disorder and it will all come together.

---

1. Cascio CN, O'Donnell MB, Tinney FJ, Lieberman MD, Taylor SE, Strecher VJ & Falk EB. Self-affirmation activates brain systems associated with self-related processing and reward and is reinforced by future orientation. Soc Cogn Affect Neurosci. 2016 Apr;11(4):621-9. doi: 10.1093/scan/nsv136. Epub 2015 Nov 5. PMID: 26541373; PMCID: PMC4814782.

Chapter 62

Gratitude

G ratitude is another valuable tool to support you to overcome an eating disorder, recognise the good in life and manage anxiety.

Before you roll your eyes and skip past this chapter (as I would have done a few years ago), hear me out. You might think that gratitude is all too woo-woo and that with an eating disorder making your life miserable, it's hard to find much to be grateful for. I get that. But firstly, there's a lot of significant research to back up gratitude practices and secondly, if you are feeling that bleak, perhaps a simple way to bring a flicker of hope is needed.

When I sat down to write this chapter, I researched the latest evidence around gratitude, its benefits and the most effective methods to use. I knew that there were significant benefits but what I learnt was that a lot of the methods people widely recommended are being superseded with new, more effective approaches. You might be familiar with approaches that involve identifying and writing down things that you are grateful for each day, perhaps while bringing your body and emotions into the feelings of thankfulness you have. It turns out though that this isn't the best method. The latest techniques recommended by neuroscientists are described below, but first, let's revise some of the benefits of practising gratitude.

The Benefits of Gratitude Practice[1]

[2]

- **To shift a negative mindset and emotions**. Gratitude can remove your attention from negative aspects of life that you might be ruminating and obsessing over, towards the positive. If you tend to obsess over the negative aspects of weight gain, gratitude could help you to reframe those thoughts and identify the good things that a bigger body brings.

- **Improves relationships.** This can be your relationship with yourself or with others. Gratitude reduces stress and anxiety which can help in your sense of self and if you have increased feelings of positivity and thankfulness towards others, it can improve the trust and loyalty in those relationships too.

- **A natural anti-depressant.** Gratitude practice stimulates your brain to release serotonin, oxytocin and dopamine which are chemicals that make you feel good. Serotonin makes you feel more relaxed and these chemicals can have the effect of making you feel that life is more possible. Regular practice leads to the development of neural pathways in your brain that will make you feel naturally calmer, more positive and motivated. When you let the eating disorder go, alongside the numbing effects it provides, gratitude practice can be a valuable tool to enable you to manage life's challenges without resorting to addictive behaviours.

- **Reduces the experience of physical pain.** This is also related to the release of key brain chemicals that affect pain responses, motivation and how energised you feel.

- **Stress and anxiety levels reduce**. This is due to the release of chemicals such as serotonin and oxytocin and is also attributed to the fact that gratitude reduces activity in your amygdala and reduces cortisol levels.

- **Better sleep.** A grateful brain will activate the hypothalamus which regulates your sleep. In this way, gratitude can make you sleep deeper and longer. Sleep is key for neuroplasticity and the reprogramming process to overcome the eating disorder—just one more key advantage.

- **Improves blood pressure, heart health and natural immunity.**

- **Makes you more optimistic, empathetic and compassionate, less materialistic and improves self-esteem**. Gratitude improves life satisfaction and a sense of increased well-being.

- **Improves anti-inflammatory markers within your body.**

How to Practice Gratitude

Now you know the benefits of gratitude practice, it's time to explore how to go about it.

Although I'm sure there are benefits to practising gratitude in ways that you might be familiar with, such as keeping a gratitude journal or sitting each evening and reflecting on a few things that you are thankful for, the latest thinking about the best way to practise gratitude is quite different.

Recommended approaches have recently been revised, based on research that shows that people gain more benefit from either receiving heartfelt gratitude from someone else or by watching or reading about a genuine exchange of gratitude. The new recommendations for how to practise gratitude are demonstrating even greater benefits.

Our brains have strong story-telling circuits which love to have a narrative for things and this is the basis of the recommended method.

1. Think of a narrative which can either be of a time that you received heartfelt thanks from someone else or of a story where you observed someone else genuinely receiving or giving thanks. If you choose the latter then it needs to be a story that resonates and inspires you.

2. Ensure you are familiar with the full narrative and can bring it to mind in detail. Write a few bullet points as reminders of the story which will be your prompt for each time you practice gratitude, so that you don't have to go through the whole story each time.

3. Your bullet point prompts should include a couple of points of what happened and reflect on the state you or the person was in before receiving gratitude and after. Add any additional elements that add an emotional tone to the story.

4. Make sure that the story is embedded in your memory and that it holds emotional meaning.

5. When you practice, remember the narrative and feel all the emotions that come with it. Use the same narrative each time and it will become easier to get into the state of feeling positive, grateful and calm.

6. Repeat regularly. It might be 3-5 times a week, any time of day and can be just one minute of practice, although research shows that up to 5 minutes has the biggest benefits. Form this into your routine and it could bring immense benefits to your life and to your ability to feel less anxious, more optimistic and motivated. You will hopefully agree

that all these things can only be advantageous as you continue to work towards overcoming the eating disorder.

Have a go. I'm sure you can find one minute, three times a week for all the benefits doing so could bring. Like anything, the benefits take time and it needs to be a regular practice but keep going and it's likely that you will soon notice yourself developing a more positive and hopeful outlook on life and on your future free of the eating disorder.

1. https://hubermanlab.com/the-science-of-grati-tude-and-how-to-build-a-gratitude-practice/

2. Tomczyk J, Nezlek JB & Krejtz I. Gratitude can help women at-risk for depression accept their depressive symptoms, which leads to improved mental health. Front Psychol. 2022 Apr 7;13:878819. doi: 10.3389/fpsy g.2022.878819. PMID: 35465539; PMCID: PMC9022718.

Chapter 63

Journaling

I widely recommend journaling as a tool, even if you do nothing else. Journaling helped me immensely as I went through the darkest days overcoming the eating disorder and I still journal regularly. It's powerful and worth adding to your armoury.

There are no rules to journaling. You don't have to do it in any particular way. You can write in a notebook or fancy journal, use a scrap of paper, journaling app or word-processing software on your computer. Find what works for you. What you write is also unimportant. You don't have to be a word-perfect, incredible writer with perfect spelling and grammar. No one ever needs to read it unless you want them to. Nothing about journaling needs to be perfect.

Write about what's happening within you, with no masks and no need to worry about hurting anyone's feelings. Just write what's on your mind. Some people like to write as if they are talking to another person but do what works for you. You might just write bullet points or single meaningful words with a lot of emotion attached to them spelt out in huge letters across the page.

Why Journal—What's the Point?

As explained repeatedly now, both in this book and in *Addicted to Energy Deficit*, eating disorders, as a form of addiction are very powerful at blocking emotions, enabling you to go through life without feeling much of anything, either good or bad. When upsetting and stressful things happen, you automatically jump to your chase of energy deficit through restriction or other behaviours for the quick hit of dopamine that so rapidly numbs you and makes you feel better. As you enter the process to overcome the eating disorder, you need other ways to deal with emotions and to process the stressful things in your life. Positive emotions can also be overwhelming when, not having experienced them for a long time, they become more intense again. Journaling can help you to process your thoughts, positive and negative emotions and apply perspective.

Research has also shown that journaling can help with low mood and anxiety[1]. It can enable you to accept rather than judge experiences or situations so you can free yourself to move forward. This can help to reduce the intensity of any negative emotions you experience in response to stressful situations. Journaling also provides several health benefits. It lowers stress, improves your immune system and long-term memory and can positively alter social behaviours.

One study looking at the use of journaling for people overcoming addictions found that it helped the participants to recognise what was positive about recovery, achieve meaningful goals and feel optimism and pride in their accomplishments[2].

Journaling can also help with the experience of gratitude, adding to the benefits this can bring (please see the previous chapter about gratitude practice).

So, there are several benefits to journaling. And they are all things that can be invaluable as you overcome an eating disorder, facing challenging situations and hard emotions. It can also help you discover who you are beyond the eating disorder, as you develop a deeper sense of identity. But how does journaling achieve all of this?

Journaling is Powerful Because:

- It confronts previously inhibited emotions.

- It helps cognitive processing, to reorganise and structure memories and situations.

- It helps with repeated exposure to situations by recalling and reflecting on them.

- It enables you to get thoughts down on paper so that you process them in an analytical way, detaching from emotive influences as you do so to work through the situations and establish the best way to move forward.

- Rather than letting negative thoughts escalate and spiral, journaling can allow you to get them out of your head and look at them in a new way, applying perspective to determine the truth about them.

- It can help you to manage difficult experiences so you confront the things you have experienced rather than avoid and not process them. Journaling stops you from numbing the pain and enables you to process and feel it instead.

Journaling is powerful in several beneficial ways. It can support you with processing and managing a lot of what you have to deal with as you overcome an eating disorder, as well as help you to reflect on the process and find ways to keep moving through it.

As I said before, journaling helps me immensely and when I recommend it to clients and they give it a go, they frequently report how useful they find it. Give it a try. Use any method that works for you. The best method will be the one you can use regularly that's practical for your life and that you feel most comfortable with. Then get writing. Get out on paper (or screen) whatever's going on deep down. Process it, feel it and keep moving forwards.

---

1. Baikie K, & Wilhelm K. Emotional and physical health benefits of expressive writing. Advances in Psychiatric Treatment. 2005;11(5), 338-346. doi:10.1192/apt.11.5.338.

2. Krentzman AR, Hoeppner BB, Hoeppner SS & Barnett NP. Development, feasibility, acceptability, and impact of a positive psychology journaling intervention to support addiction recovery. The Journal of Positive Psychology. 2022; DOI: 10.1080/17439760.2022.2070531.

Chapter 64

Daily intentions

Setting daily or weekly intentions will help you to stay focused on your eating disorder-bashing goals, keeping them a priority so that you maintain momentum.

It's easy to say, *I'm going to abstain from all restriction, stop all unnecessary movement, not purge and aim for overshoot,* but then struggle to establish what that looks like and how to keep building on the progress that you've made. You might find that you fall into new routines that are better than they were when you were deeply entrenched in the eating disorder but you still aren't facing all the necessary new situations, experiences and challenges that you want to be able to do with ease in future. It can therefore help to set positive intentions and share them with a support person for accountability or just have them for yourself to keep you focused.

Overall, there are several benefits to setting daily or weekly intentions as you are overcoming the eating disorder. These include:

- maintaining your focus on your overall goals when the long process becomes exhausting and other things in life are distracting you;

- holding onto the progress you have made and continuing to build on it;

- setting a tone of positivity and purpose about what you are doing and why;

- a means to give yourself permission to do the things that you intended but that create anxiety and doubts in the moment;

- helping you to address your perceived limitations or obstacles;

- enabling you to think more widely, consider possibilities and avoid falling into new routines or the trap of thinking, *I've gained some weight, eat more and no longer exercise so I'm doing enough;*

- keeping you in the present moment, not getting caught up in the past or future;

- enabling you to track your progress and recognise your wins;

- providing a form of accountability;

- ensuring you are repeating new experiences and building on them to enable more complete and successful brain rewiring;

- motivating and empowering you;

- improving your self-belief.

As you can see, setting intentions has many benefits. Your intentions can be just for you or you can share them with others. But whether you share them or not, they can give you something to focus on, prioritise and be used to empower you to build your future.

Below are some examples of intentions that you might set to overcome an eating disorder:

Today I will go to lunch with my friend and order a meal that's not a salad, has lots of fats and triple carbs, with dessert and I won't compensate before or after.

I will go shopping for clothes that I feel like me in and make my body feel good, letting myself spend the money and ignoring any guilt about doing so.

This weekend, I'll rest on the couch each day, eating all the foods my brain and body ask me for, ignoring any thoughts that arise trying to pull me away from doing so. I'll remind myself that this is for my future life and it's the most important thing I can be doing right now.

Make setting daily intentions a habit so that you stay focused and on track. This process is long and it's easy to lose momentum after a couple of weeks or months when, in reality, that momentum is needed for a lot longer.

Put aside some time each day that you will use to set your intentions either for that day or the next. Very often our brains are the most relaxed in the evenings before bed, so this can be the best time to set positive and focused intentions for the next day that you can then wake up and make happen with glee!

Chapter 65

Why Your WHY Matters!

B uild your *why* for overcoming the eating disorder and it's another thing that can help you to stay motivated, focused and determined when the urges to race back to old behaviours become overpowering or your anxiety response is high.

I've said it before and I'll say it again—overcoming an eating disorder is likely to be the hardest thing you do in your lifetime. And it's generally recognised that when we are working towards any big goal or life outcome and progress gets tough, it's a much greater struggle to keep going without a very powerful reason or *why* to do so.

Grit, determination or stubborn-mindedness will only ever get you so far. To get through the tough days as you pursue your life free of the eating disorder, you need to deeply connect to the reasons for what you are doing. This needs to be emotive and meaningful to you. If your reasons to overcome the eating disorder are merely external, such as because someone else is pressuring you or even offering you some form of monetary or other reward for doing so, the lack of emotional power behind these incentives will reduce their impact.

It's said that 95% of our day-to-day decisions are guided by our emotions and whatever feels good in the moment, while just 5% of the decisions that guide our actions stem from reason or logic. These figures might not be completely accurate but there's still a lot of truth to them. For the best chance of your day-to-day decisions leading to action towards your goals, you need a meaningful *why* or you will have a constant internal battle between your rational and emotional brain.

As humans, we seek and need connection, fulfilment and purpose. These inner needs and values can be a good place to start as you reflect on your *why* for your eating disorder-bashing goals. When things get tough, you'll need to be emotionally connected to why you can and will tolerate the bumps in your journey.

Finding Your *Why*

To tap into and find your deeply intrinsic and value-driven *why* for overcoming the eating disorder, ask yourself a few questions:

- Why do you want to focus on overcoming the eating disorder and not something else in your life?

- Why is it worth the hard work and sacrifice?

- What will achieving a future without an eating disorder bring to you?

- What might achieving it bring to the life of other people?

- Is overcoming the eating disorder a true *want* for you or is it a *should*? (if it's a should then you might need to rethink it).

Spend time, perhaps with your eyes closed, allowing your mind to wander and exploring your authentic WHY. Create an image of what it will look and feel like when you have found a free life without the eating disorder in it, allowing yourself to experience it in full depth and colour, letting it be emotive. Then hold onto the images and emotions that came through and write them out in detail. Build a vision of your future self who is free of the eating disorder, living their best life and use it to propel you towards all you need to do to become that person.

When you are in the thick of the process and things are feeling tough or you have powerful urges to run back to the eating disorder, keep coming back to this *why* and the vision you built. Hold onto the meaning, purpose and emotions that underlie why you are putting yourself through this to find the momentum to keep going.

When you can see the potential end results of overcoming the eating disorder as something you really want to achieve, identifying with your *why,* and when the necessary changes you are making stop being something you feel you *should* do, then eating disorder-bashing feels less like hard work and more like (dare I say it) fun!

Chapter 66

Taking Time Out Now So Life Doesn't Time Out On You

One thing that people with eating disorders excel at is their addictive drive to go, go, go like a Duracell bunny with batteries that keep going on very little charge and seem to never run out... Except even the best Duracell bunny only keeps going so long and someday even your batteries will go flat and you might not get a low-charge warning light.

You and your loved ones might think that things can't be *that bad* because perhaps you have a high-powered job, maybe even working more than full-time or you have ongoing academic accolades. Maybe you can run a home and family life while pursuing said job and/or academic pursuits. If you don't work, perhaps you spend the days on the go, keeping busy and active in any number of ways that feel incredibly important and productive.

To all intents and purposes, you can appear at a surface level to be a high achiever—driven, successful and accomplished. Surely then all this talk about the eating disorder being such a powerful addiction doesn't apply to you? And if it does, considering how seemingly easily you can do everything else, taking on a little thing like overcoming an eating disorder is surely just a small addition to your daily *to-do* list and shouldn't be an issue? *No worries,* you might say, *I'll just eat and rest a bit more, gain some weight and carry on with everything else because stopping the other things just can't happen.*

But, the reality is that:

1. The busy life you have created with your career, academia, compulsive behaviours, incredible home and seemingly being able to juggle it all, is largely driven by a brain that's addicted to energy deficit. It's stemming from the evolutionary response to famine*, so your brain is keeping you constantly busy in the hope you will use this high-energy drive and restlessness to find food. Because your go, go, go drive is addictive and part of the eating disorder, you need to address it just as much as you need to address all other aspects of the eating disorder.

2. Overcoming an eating disorder takes more focus and mental energy than anything else you will do in your life. Any accomplishments that you have achieved in your life up until now will seem easy compared to the mental, emotional and physical repair work you need to do to overcome the eating disorder. While still focusing all your attention each day on a job, studies or other pursuits, you won't have the brain space to apply to abstaining from restriction, stopping yourself from engaging in compulsive and deeply entrenched habits or allowing yourself to feel the necessary emotions that arise or respond to the exhaustion that's likely to hit. You are kidding yourself by thinking you will just eat a bit more and overcome the eating disorder but keep the rest of your life as it is and you are unlikely to get far. You might make a tiny change here and there, but it's going to be incredibly hard to achieve anything meaningful or lasting (sorry).

Taking time out and giving yourself as much time as you can to focus on the work of overcoming the eating disorder, purposefully taking steps to reprogram your brain and emerge from energy deficit, can be the deciding factor in whether you succeed or not.

The people I see make significant progress in just a few months are those who give themselves the life space to do it. Those who convince themselves and everyone around them that they can *do recovery* while continuing all their other life pursuits are generally still chipping away in a two-step forward, one or two-step back dance a year later. And no one wants that. You deserve to be living your best life as soon as possible, not still addictively driven, living a narrowed life and hungry in another two years, all because you thought that taking a few months out of your career would be a worse fate.

I'm sure that you now have a million arguments coming up about why you can't take time out. Money is likely to be a big one because, for one thing, the scarcity mindset will be impacting you and yes, the cost of living is a factor. But very often people can find ways to make things work financially when they problem-solve and seek solutions. For the students amongst you, you might be thinking that taking time out of university now will mean that you miss out on x, y, z opportunities which won't be there again, or perhaps this relates to a work or promotion opportunity. Trust me though, as someone who learnt these lessons the hard way, there are always more exciting life opportunities to be found and when you are free of the eating disorder, you will be able to embrace them in more meaningful ways than you ever can now. Plus, you might find that your interests and career goals change entirely as you evolve as a person when the eating disorder isn't narrowing you, leaving you wanting to seek out life pursuits you can't even imagine at the moment. Please, don't forsake your life potential for the sake of your perceived career potential.

Those of you with families are perhaps thinking that you can't stop being the super-parent, partner and home-keeper that you are now. However, I can guarantee that you can ramp it down a few notches and find ways for your family's needs to be met, while you continue to do what's necessary to be the kind of parent and partner for your family that you can't be with an eating disorder.

And if you have other persuasive thoughts and emotional resistance to the thought of taking time out from your life to focus on overcoming the eating disorder, reflect on where the resistance is coming from. It's very likely stemming from an addicted brain terrified of being challenged. Because the thought of taking time out means you have no excuse not to do the things necessary to address the eating disorder and that's terrifying to a brain that desperately needs its fix several times a day from the ongoing pursuit of energy deficit.

Internal resistance is your in-built sat-nav for the direction you need to take. Therefore, allowing yourself time out to focus on overcoming the eating disorder might be a terrifying thought and necessitate some significant life changes for a while, but perhaps that's because it might actually work?

As I said at the beginning, every Duracell bunny only lasts so long. And that will be true for you too if you keep going and going with the eating disorder. Yes, you might continue to be successful, accomplished and fly through your narrow life on a high of energy deficit for years but at some point, your batteries will stop, perhaps without any warning. I've known too many people whose batteries stopped and they didn't know it was coming. Don't let that be you because *it will never happen to me* is something they said too.

Fully review your current life and reflect with honesty on the commitments you have that can be dropped for a while, minimising the things you need to focus on beyond the work to overcome the eating disorder as far as possible. Speak to family, friends, health professionals, your employer or tutors, a coach or anyone necessary to problem solve any practical issues there might be to you stopping some things for a time. Allow people to support you—seek help. Don't see this as being unnecessary or feel any guilt or shame in needing to give yourself this space. Take this time out and use it productively to make the necessary changes and prioritise the recovery work (because it is work) needed to let the eating disorder go. If you were overcoming something else as life-limiting or that had the same potentially devastating consequences as an eating disorder, you would give yourself the time needed to address it. Treat this the same way, so you are the best version of yourself that you can be, living a truly fulfilling life in no time, which will be incredible for you and amazing for those who care about you.

When I first developed an eating disorder and was advised to take time out, I resisted, thinking I didn't need to. I believed I could continue to work and eat a few Mars bars and hey presto, I'd be fine. At that time someone said to me, *But what's a few short months of time-out now for the sake of the rest of your life?* That question stayed with me for all these years, perhaps because it was advice I regret not taking when I learnt the hard way that they were right. And so I put the same question to you today:

> *What's a few short months of time-out now, for the sake of the rest of your life?*

Invest in your future so you have so much more life potential, with freedom, joy and yes, the ability to really have fun in your life as well!

See Addicted to Energy Deficit if you want to understand more about the evolutionary, Flee-from-Famine theory to restrictive eating disorders

Chapter 67

Making Other Valuable Life Adjustments

The value of making other life adjustments to give you the optimal circumstances and support for success at overcoming the eating disorder is something else worth taking time to think about.

There are several life adjustments that you might consider putting in place, some of which tie into taking time away from your other life commitments, alongside other equally important considerations.

It can't be reiterated enough that the process of fully overcoming an eating disorder is hard work, exhausting and emotional. It's a journey of self-discovery and building a future that you feel fully connected to. Some life adjustments, either in the short or long term, can make or break whether you do find a full and authentic life without the eating disorder affecting you or whether you get so far but then burn out (see Chapter 38).

To achieve the things that are most important to us in life and reap the biggest rewards, short-term sacrifices (or what can feel like sacrifices in the moment) are often necessary. Or perhaps there are changes that you know have been needed for some time but haven't dared make them before. Now is the time to put in place life adjustments that you instinctively know will make your ability to get through this process easier, even if they are difficult or disruptive in the short term. The best things we can do in life are often the hardest.

What kind of life adjustments am I referring to?

Below are some examples that you might want to consider. Of course, they won't all apply to you, perhaps none of the examples given do, but you might be able to think of others that you know would help. Take this as your green light to follow your instincts and do it.

Possible Life Adjustments Needed to Overcome an Eating Disorder:

- Some people need to make adjustments to ensure sufficient in-person support. For example, if you are at university or you've moved away from family and friendship circles for work, leaving you more isolated, then you might need to move back to be closer to family or friends for a while for critical social support. *Addicted to Energy Deficit* explains why connection to others when you are overcoming an eating disorder is so important. The value of having connection and support should not be underestimated. Even if the people you seek closer connection with can't provide intense support with the process, just having emotional support or someone who can be with you after eating to distract you from the temptation to purge, can make all the difference. And please don't allow any shame to creep in if you do decide to move in with your parents or other family members as you go through this. Many people say that because they are an adult, they shouldn't need to rely on or seek support from their family, but you absolutely should. Plus, if it's either using their support and overcoming the eating disorder to enable stronger and fuller relationships with them in your future, or letting shame stop you from doing so, resulting in your not overcoming the eating disorder, which would you rather?

- Some people have built their lives around the eating disorder and made career choices that were influenced by it, or their career gave rise to their initial encounter with energy deficit, leading to the development and then entrenchment of the eating disorder. Again this is covered in more depth in *Addicted to Energy Deficit*, but examples might be people who have careers in sports, fitness, health or the food industry. When this is the case, going back to your past career might either carry too much risk or be so entwined in the eating disorder and related memories that it's not something you want to consider. This means taking time from these pursuits now, as you overcome the eating disorder, and allowing yourself to explore new and exciting options for your future that you know speak to your true passions and values.

- Changing your friendship groups and social networks can also be necessary in some cases. If your social circles are largely based around health, fitness or other interests influenced by diet culture, which will be unnecessary triggers, then you'll want to consider finding alternative groups to connect to and enjoy spending time with. Of course, this isn't easy to do, but as you discover who you are away from the eating disorder, you will likely feel less connected to those who are still deeply entrenched in diet culture values and you will want to find meaningful friendships with people who have values that align with your own.

- Eating disorders take up a lot of time, using your free moments to engage in behaviours and pursuits that are compulsive and following hobbies and interests which are likely those of the eating disorder, rather than your own. When you stop these behaviours, you open up time in your day and your life to gradually explore and discover ways to spend time that do interest you. Dabble in new interests and experiment with social groups and hobbies that are not related to exercise, fitness, food or diet culture.

- For a few, overcoming the eating disorder and being true to your authentic self, will necessitate moving away from relationships which aren't right for you. It might be that the eating disorder served as a way to numb that reality from yourself and to overcome the eating disorder you now need to address it. If you are in a relationship, be that with a partner, family members, friends, or even an employer or business partner, which deep down you know isn't right for you and believe you need to detach from, you will need to explore the steps to take. These situations are always difficult but you can choose to step away from those connections for a time, while you find out who you are and become stronger without the eating disorder, allowing yourself the space to reflect on what is right for you and your relationships beyond it.

- Allowing others to help and support you in meaningful ways is an-other adjustment that's important to put into place. Sometimes the biggest life skill we can learn is to be vulnerable and ask for support. Don't try to do everything yourself while going through what might be the biggest challenge of your life. Ask for help with childcare, housework and other responsibilities that you usually take on. Use your partner if you have one, wider family or friends, or seek paid help for a while. You need all the time you can get to rest, eat and apply the mental focus and energy that overcoming the eating disorder demands. Let others help and take this critical time out.

- Finally, learning to say no to people when saying yes to their requests will mean you can't focus on what's needed to overcome the eating disorder is something you might not find easy but that will also serve you well. Don't say yes to things that will mean saying no to recovery! People with eating disorders are excellent at being seemingly selfless, putting everyone else's needs before their own and letting the martyr complex take over (this is a key trait of a restrictive eating disorder, covered in detail in *Addicted to Energy Deficit*). The problem is that while you keep saying yes to the demands of others, leaving your ability to put in the work needed that day to overcome the eating disorder by the wayside, your ability to live a valuable life in future, able to give back to the world in ways you can't now, remains out of reach.

These are just a few life adjustments worth careful consideration as you do the work to overcome the eating disorder, optimising your chances of success. Changes like these are hard to make and some are life-changing but change is often a good thing. Recognise the strength in asking for help or being vulnerable and the importance it has in helping you move forwards. View recovery as the most valuable opportunity—one that most people never get—to truly discover yourself and build your life, even if that is from the ground up, into one that fully aligns with your values and authentic self.

Change can be hard but not as hard as living with an eating disorder, so we both know that you can do hard things.

Chapter 68

Avoid the Trap of the Rose-Tinted Glasses

When the withdrawal effects and cravings from giving up the eating disorder and its associated behaviours become overwhelming, leaving you with high levels of agitation, crippling anxiety and feeling very low, your brain is guaranteed to generate thoughts along the lines of, *Living with the eating disorder wasn't THAT bad; in fact, it was really ok; I was wrong to think I needed to overcome it.*

The rose-tinted glasses will come on, you will forget how miserable you were with the eating disorder, exaggerate any tiny positive it might have had (or invent some) and feel tempted to go back. This is only natural. When your current reality has become intensely painful and you don't know when the benefits of continuing to move forward with recovery will come, going back to a life in which you know you can feel numb and at least function on a very basic level will be attractive.

Rationally, you and I know why this is happening and that if you keep moving forward, the painful withdrawal effects will pass, the cravings will subside and life will become more possible than it ever has been. But when you are in the depths of the pain, your rational side is likely to go offline and you will need other instant reminders for why you do want to tolerate these tough days and keep going. Therefore, when you are in a state of feeling calm and rational, create a list of all the ways that the eating disorder made your life hell and the destructive impact it had on you, your wider life and your loved ones.

Do a brainstorm and write it all down, including all the details you can. Hold nothing back. This list has to be powerful and persuasive for times when you are going to be very vulnerable and at risk of a lapse. It's therefore important you speak to your future self with heartfelt reasons for why you don't want to stop or return to the eating disorder.

Journal about it or make your reasons into a big list that you stick on the wall, adding pictures and colour. Do whatever you think will help you when you are in a highly emotive and anxious state.

The eating disorder was miserable. It made you so unhappy that you decided to embark on this process and you had strong reasons for that. Recall them all and keep adding to them, continuously reminding yourself what they were.

The trap of the rose-tinted glasses is one of the biggest reasons that people relapse from eating disorders and other addictions. Don't be another one of its victims.

Chapter 69

Remember Fun?!?

A brain with a deeply entrenched eating disorder or any other form of addiction has much less capacity to experience fun or pleasure from other things in life. The eating disorder itself is likely to have made your life very miserable and the kinds of things that give others enjoyment can be much less pleasurable to an energy deficit-addicted brain.

You've likely become very good at laughing to fit in with what's expected in social company but rarely with a genuine and joyful belly laugh. As you are overcoming the eating disorder and your narrowed focus opens up to the ability to experience pleasure again in all kinds of things, it's vital to find ways to rediscover the fun in life. Because fun in life is very important!

First though, what is *fun*?

Fun is most recognisable in children who are easily swept along in moments of pure enjoyment–guilt-free and innocent. To have fun means to be in the moment, putting worries about other things aside. It's letting go of your inhibitions and not being scared to be seen as silly. Those concerns only hold you back from letting go and finding pure joy in the moment. Fun commonly also involves imagination and creativity.

Although it's possible to have fun alone, the chances of finding fun or laughing are vastly increased when you spend time with other people. The common belief that children laugh more than adults isn't that simple. The amount anyone laughs is dependent on the number of social interactions they have, irrespective of age[1].

It's not just people with eating disorders who lose touch with the life skill of fun, although an eating disorder will affect you more than most. But when you do lose your ability for fun, so much suffers. When you stop having fun, you stop being the best possible version of yourself and then everyone misses out.

Therefore, it's time to reclaim the fun in your life and here's why:

- Fun and laughter can reduce stress and anxiety by increasing levels of the feel-good chemicals in your brain and reducing levels of the stress hormones throughout your body.

- Fun improves levels of depression, makes you sleep better and can even help improve your memory.

- Fun and laughter improve physical pain perceptions and improve your immunity, tumour markers and risks of heart disease and diabetes.

- Just a smile in a moment triggers your brain to release neuropeptides which also help combat stress and boost endorphins, serotonin and dopamine which make you feel good in yourself.

- Fun through play is shown to protect your brain from degeneration—age-related brain disorders can be delayed through fun games and activities.

- And, if you think you are too busy to have fun—it's been demonstrated that workers who take time to have fun are more energised, creative and productive in their work.

It's valuable to explore ways to experience fun again as you overcome the eating disorder and to build more feel-good positivity into your life with things that are not related to the addicted pursuit of energy deficit. This will improve your capacity to connect to your authentic self and develop an identity beyond the eating disorder.

What About Play?

Dr. Stuart Brown is a psychiatrist, clinical researcher, founder of the National Institue of Play and generally considered a play expert[2]. Fun often stems from play and as such he recognises that play isn't just important for children, for whom play is critical to healthy brain development, but throughout the lifespan.

When looking at the brain in response to play, Dr. Brown's research has found that the brain circuits responding to play triggers are located in the same deep survival centres as hunger circuits. He stipulates that play is a physiological necessity in the same way as sleep. In fact, the higher brain region (the pre-frontal cortex) doesn't need to be engaged for you to enjoy and have fun in play but the act of play itself can help to shape and develop your pre-frontal cortex.

Play is also seen to improve quality of life, decrease stress, help you feel connected to a community, reduce feelings of loneliness and promote optimism and empathy. Dr. Brown stipulates that lifelong brain plasticity (the ability of the brain to continue to learn and change) is *primed by playfulness* and although your approach to play might change as you age, overcoming your inhibitions and finding ways to add more play into your life at any age can only be a good thing.

A quote that summarises Dr. Brown's message is,

The opposite to play is not work but is depression.

Dr. Stuart Brown

When overcoming the eating disorder feels long, emotional and exhausting, adding some playfulness can make a difference. It can make the process more stimulating, engage your brain in ways that are more likely to be wired in and reduce the anxiety or low mood you might be experiencing.

Setting yourself challenges with your eating, resting or how fully you can aim for overshoot, applying a sense of playful curiosity to the process and playfully seeing how many smarties are in a giant tube while you consume them all, removes some of the seriousness from the process.

Perhaps it's time to rediscover the ability to do something just for the sheer pleasure of it and for no other reason—pursuits that will have you happily losing your sense of time and living entirely in the moment. Adopt curiosity and creativity to find focus and passion for things in your life that will bring more fun to it.

Rediscover your childhood self and allow their sense of playfulness and pleasure to resurface. Your self-identity is also important in your ability to find more fun. As you build your identity beyond the eating disorder, start to identify as someone who is and has fun. Believe this of yourself and let the fun and playfulness in. It's ok to be a bit wild and free sometimes!

And if you would like my recipe for adding more fun to your life, here it is:
Adopt a little Feck it attitude;
Become more Uninhibited; and
Nurture your inner child!!

1. https://aath.memberclicks.net/do-children-laugh-much-more-often-than-adults-do/

2. https://www.nifplay.org/about-us/about-nifp/

Chapter 70

A Tool to Develop Your Self-Trust

It's almost guaranteed that with the eating disorder, you have found yourself in regular cycles of saying, *Tomorrow I will change*, only to then find that tomorrow is no different to today. When this happens repeatedly it can erode any trust you have in yourself and your abilities.

But self-trust is an important quality to develop as you overcome an eating disorder. It becomes easier to make the necessary changes when you do have trust in your ability to make those changes and achieve a free life. Yes, your trust in yourself will naturally increase when you do make changes and realise that you can, but a simple tool to increase and nurture your self-trust can help.

Consider the hard things you have done in your life and what you have achieved or overcome in your past. Use this to remind yourself that you can do hard things and you can trust yourself.

Then, couple this with a technique that involves allowing your future self to take control of what you do today. Create a picture of a future you—someone who is in the life you hope for, free of the eating disorder, stronger for having come through it and proud. Allow your future self to take control of you now.

Ultimately this imagined future self is you, so merge that person with who you are now, allow your authentic self to emerge and let your self-trust grow from it.

When the urge to restrict or turn down the side of fries sets in, allow your future self to make the decisions and lead you towards the future you are meant to have. Let yourself accept the short-term pain of not restricting today for the longer-term gain of not having an eating disorder in a year or two from now. Remind yourself that your future health and ability to enjoy a full and meaningful life free of the eating disorder is sacrificed if you opt for instant gratification today by engaging in compulsive behaviours or the pursuit of energy deficit. Believe instead in your ability to take control and abstain from the eating disorder's addictive behaviours and rituals and do it. As your self-trust grows, so too does the possibility to make even more changes.

Chapter 71

Let's Talk About Lapses & Relapses

A topic that no one wants to think about is sliding backwards when you have made progress in overcoming the eating disorder—whether it's a slide back while you are still on the trajectory from deep entrenchment to freedom or after you have found a free life. *Addicted to Energy Deficit* includes an explanation of the differences between a relapse, lapse and pre-lapse, what's happening in your brain if you do relapse and the importance of recognising the signs early.

In my view, people who have fully (and not just partially) overcome restrictive eating disorders are at low risk of relapse because of the work, self-reflection and self-awareness they have gained during the process. The knowledge they gain about the risks of diet culture makes them much less susceptible to those risks and more resistant to diet culture's messages than most. But anyone with a history of a restrictive eating disorder will carry genetic susceptibility, meaning that the risk is always there for the eating disorder to return if exposed to the right combination of risk factors. The biggest of these risks is re-entering a state of energy deficit but high levels of stress or emotion or facing a powerful old trigger can also be factors to reignite lingering eating disorder brain networks that have lain dormant but not fully broken down.

Staying safely out of energy deficit for the rest of your life, not trying to manipulate or suppress your natural body weight or shape and embracing your curves will help to ensure you stay eating disorder free. Developing and maintaining excellent self-awareness so that you can recognise any signs of things sliding back and rapidly act if you do notice anything, no matter how small, is also important. This high level of self-awareness and self-reflection is especially critical in the first few years when you are still consolidating the brain re-programming you have achieved.

But it's not just a relapse you need awareness of. Lapses are also a risk. A *relapse* relates to when you have all but overcome the eating disorder, while *lapses* can occur when you are still in the process of overcoming it. This is because the journey is long, often exhausting and life can get in the way.

Become an expert at noticing when you have taken your foot off the gas with your eating disorder-bashing efforts and when you are starting to either tread water in a way that's becoming a bit too comfortable or you have started down a backward slippery slope. You can't afford any loss in momentum in this process or before you know it, your addicted brain will be back in the driving seat, pushing you back into the energy deficit-seeking behaviours that give you a soothing dopamine rush. The ability to quickly spot the signs that things are sliding and rapidly address them can make the difference between living the free life you deserve forever or not.

Chapter 72

Signs of a Lapse or Relapse

C onstant vigilance is required to maintain momentum in overcoming an eating disorder. It can be easy to get distracted from eating disorder-bashing and not notice that disordered thoughts and urges are creeping back when, after years of eating disorder misery, life has more meaning again and you just want to enjoy it. Therefore, you need to recognise the signs that things are going *off-kilter,* reminding you to slow down and put your focus back onto eating disorder-bashing so that ultimately, you really can enjoy your life.

Below are some typical warning signs of when an eating disorder and its addictive nature is becoming stronger again—signs telling you to recommit to your goal of aiming for overshoot and to remove any risk of a lapse or relapse.

Common Signs of a Lapse or Relapse

- Increased restriction—your food intake is sliding, you are eating predominantly *safe* foods and avoiding fears or there's more rigidity to how, what and when you eat.

- More thoughts and urges that relate to your eating, exercise or other compensatory behaviours.

- Feeling overwhelmed by things that you have to do or events in your life, whether they involve bashing the eating disorder or not.

- Worsening body image—an increase in thoughts about or focus on your body shape and weight.

- Urges to weigh yourself, particularly if this has been compulsive before.

- A stronger fear of weight gain and becoming increasingly attracted to the thought of weight loss.

- Signs of weight loss that you experience a sense of achievement or reward from.

- An increasing need for *control,* commonly with your food intake but with other aspects of your life too.

- Isolating yourself more from others.

- A rise in negative thought patterns, self-talk and emotions.

- Conversely to the above, an increased feeling of numbness or even calmness that feels welcome.

- A return of the starvation high—the feeling of being invincible and able to fly through life.

- Feeling physically colder.

- An increasing sense of despair with your life and the future.

- Being more irritable and losing touch with the ability to find pleasure and fun.

- An increased focus on numbers, whether related to weight, calories, macros, steps or anything else.

- A growing need to control your money spending, stronger urges to save and an increased feeling of guilt over spending even small amounts.

- Increasing lower-level movement and difficulty with sitting down.

- Thoughts about taking up strength-training, bodybuilding, yoga or pilates.

- More food thoughts, aka mental hunger, which reduces your concentration elsewhere.

- Lower physical appetite and/or increased anxiety at physical hunger.

- An increase in binge eating episodes—a sign your body is not getting enough food and your energy deficit is escalating.

- Stronger cravings again for sugary foods—a sign your body is seeking instant energy sources.

- Spending more time seeking magic answers online, through social media, blogs, YouTube etc.

- Increasing mental gymnastics and negotiations, making eating and life more complicated than it should be.

- More awareness of how much you ate or engaged in compensatory behaviours yesterday, with a strong drive to ensure that today you don't eat more or compensate less.

These are some common signs and symptoms of a lapse or relapse. Learn to recognise your unique warning signs. What thoughts, urges or emotions commonly come up for you when things are starting to slide? Make a note of them so you are more likely to spot them early and can quickly take action to get things back on track.

Overcoming an eating disorder is tough. No matter where in the process you are when the eating disorder's urges and cravings start to escalate, it can still be hard work to pull things back. The distress and anxiety can be just as intense, especially if your dopamine levels have escalated through your re-engagement in old habits. This might result in a need to re-enter the dopamine deficit state and associated negative emotions to allow your dopamine level to rebalance again (see *Addicted to Energy Deficit* to understand the dopamine seesaw).

When you notice a lapse or relapse has occurred, recommit to abstaining from restrictive eating, all compensatory behaviours and rituals and to aiming for overshoot. You didn't come this far to let things go backwards now. Push against every fibre of your being that might be screaming at you not to eat or rest more or to break the rules the eating disorder creates. Do what feels so wrong, knowing it's right.

And while you are recommitting, take a moment to reflect on what might have triggered this lapse or relapse:

- have you been under more stress?

- are you getting busier?

- have your activity levels unintentionally increased or has your intake slipped?

- has something happened to make you more emotional?

- have you had a return of some memories, faced a situation or seen someone that has always been a powerful trigger?

Try to work out the cause of this lapse, so you can then establish how to protect against the same thing happening in future.

For your best chance of long-term success at overcoming the eating disorder, keep aiming for overshoot and avoid taking on too many life commitments too soon so that your focus can stay where it's needed. The final stages of physical restoration to reach overshoot and let your body heal can be the most difficult. Remind yourself that every stage of the process is as important as the beginning to maintain momentum until you are confident that your brain is fully reprogramming and your body is settling at your healthy set-point level (having allowed for overshoot). When you reach this mental and physical state of freedom, the world will be your oyster.

Chapter 73

Five Principles of Relapse Prevention

As you approach an eating disorder-free life, there are some principles to live by that will help to prevent you from returning to eating disorder misery. Below are five principles[1] that no matter where you are in the process, are worth putting in place now and maintaining as you sail into your future.

1) Change your Life

You don't overcome an eating disorder by eating more and disengaging from a few behaviours alone. It takes creating a life that makes it more possible to change your habits and live without the eating disorder. As you go through the process, the aspects of your life that kept you holding onto the compulsive habits need addressing. Big or small changes can be necessary, which might also need to be permanent. Change is always hard but these changes bring the opportunity for a happier life than you have had for a long time. And this is where having an eating disorder can have a silver lining. When you take the time to re-evaluate your life and make positive changes, you can live more authentically than most people ever will. I know that I wouldn't be living the life I live today if I hadn't had the eating disorder, so in a strange way, that makes me grateful for it, despite all it took from me. Don't view change as bad. It can feel overwhelming, but it can make a big difference and without life changes, your risk of relapse might always be present (see Chapter 67).

2) Complete Honesty

Success in overcoming an eating disorder can depend on being honest with yourself and your support team. Eating disorders often create a denial of how big a problem there is and how many of the behaviours are part of the addictive patterns. Only when you learn to be honest with yourself first and then with your support people can you fully address everything necessary. Having people you can keep talking to and remain very honest with, even after you feel you have all but *recovered*, can help you stay free. Telling others when you feel stressed, anxious and overwhelmed or feel things are sliding will help to ensure you get support early and give you a better chance of avoiding the risk of relapse.

3) Ask for Help

In conjunction with principle two, asking for help and staying connected to people who can support you matters. It would be surprising if anyone overcomes an eating disorder without support from others. *Addicted to Energy Deficit* covers how critical having support and not being isolated is. Holding onto support and pushing aside any shame or embarrassment at asking for help will go a long way in keeping you mentally and physically stable in your future.

4) Practice Self-Care

Tell me to practice self-care in the past and I'd have wanted to poke you in the eye. But self-care matters; or as I like to call it, It's *all about me time* (I like to call a spade a spade!). The eating disorder has served as a powerful emotion regulation tool and a way to manage stress for as long as it has been part of your life. Other ways to manage challenging emotions will be necessary as you let the eating disorder go. If you have habitually been someone with low self-esteem or who is very self-critical, then the ability to adopt self-care practices is also key. Self-care is about taking the time you need for yourself so that you can be the best version of yourself for others. Find ways that help you to feel better and allow you to switch off and focus on yourself, how you feel and what's happening within. It might be having a bath or massage, time to read a book with some chocolate or going to sit by water and in nature for a while. Whatever you do, take time for yourself regularly, putting dates in your diary if necessary so that it happens.

5) Don't Bend the Rules

Nope, not the eating disorder rules you have lived by for years but the rules to get and stay eating disorder free. These are staying out of energy deficit with ongoing abstinence from restriction and compensatory behaviours while resting and relaxing all you can. It also means recognising if the eating disorder is out of your life or where it's holding on. Notice if you do still wish for a smaller body and use sneaky behaviours now and then in the hope it might happen or if you have a thought at the back of your mind that you will keep eating and resting for x amount of time but after that will do as you please and this plan is reassuring to you. When you recognise signs the eating disorder is holding on, continue to work on your brain reprogramming, using support to do so.

1. Melemis SM. Relapse prevention and the five rules of recovery. Yale J Biol Med. 2015 Sep 3;88(3):325-32. PMID: 26339217; PMCID: PMC4553654.

Chapter 74

Common Pitfalls to Overcoming a Restrictive Eating Disorder

There are several risks when it comes to overcoming an eating disorder, many of which have already been covered in depth both in this book and *Addicted to Energy Deficit*. Factors such as the scales, diet culture, past trauma and difficult emotions, keeping too busy, holding onto limiting beliefs, taking on a victim mindset or settling for a half-life *quasi*-existence are just a few of the risks already discussed. This chapter describes some other common pitfalls to the quest of aiming for overshoot and finding freedom. These are things that on the surface might seem insignificant but that can have a big impact.

Common Pitfalls to Overcoming a Restrictive Eating Disorder:

The Grazing Trap

This is a pitfall that I fell into and I see it regularly in others. You decide you will eat more, abstain from restriction and so you do start eating more frequently, trying to eat each time you think of food, which is great. You break timing rules and allow yourself to eat at sporadic times of the day and night. But you then realise that in eating more frequently, you are choosing relatively small snacks each time and these have replaced the bigger meals you were having before. You feel like you are eating more because you are constantly grazing now but when you take a step back and look at your overall intake, it isn't much more than it was—you have just spread it out and made different choices. The solution is to ensure that you have big multi-course meals at least three times a day and eat big snacks whenever mental hunger strikes—every 10 minutes if that's needed to satiate it. And for those who have the opposite pattern of eating three meals but not allowing yourself snacks—you know what you need to do too!

The Whack-a-Mole Game

This is covered in *Addicted to Energy Deficit*, it just isn't titled as such. This is when you find yourself addressing one aspect of the eating disorder, such as eating more but as you do, you realise that you have started to engage in more movement or your use of laxatives has increased. This is a common pitfall in overcoming any addiction where there are multiple addictive behaviours. If your brain cannot meet its dopamine *fix* from one route, it will pursue another. The game of whack-a-mole can be tiring and frustrating. It's because of this risk that I advocate for abstaining from all behaviours together and determinedly aiming for overshoot, doing all that a person with that intent would do. This way, those pesky moles stay firmly in the ground.

Eating More But Only If...

Your brain will slowly adapt to you eating more and begin to trust that more food is ok, reducing the anxiety response it creates to specific new situations you face. But it won't let you comfortably eat more in any situation if it hasn't been exposed to it before. In this way, you can become very comfortable eating lots more within certain contexts but still find it incredibly hard to eat anything, anywhere. An example of this is that you might start cooking for yourself and preparing your own food as you abstain from restriction and do well with eating more to emerge from energy deficit. But you still find it very hard to let someone else cook for you or eat out. Or the opposite can be true. You might become very comfortable eating out in restaurants, fast-food places or takeaways but you have a high anxiety response to cooking for yourself or letting a loved one cook for you. Therefore, as you eat more, make sure you expose yourself to a wide variety of situations, foods and contexts.

A Need to Control or Inability to Trust Yourself

Some people find that eating more and breaking other habits goes well but only if they can control the whole process. Self-empowerment has been high-lighted as a critical component to overcoming an eating disorder and this isn't to deny that, but if that level of control is so extreme that you can't let your family decide what you will all eat for dinner or you flare up at the suggestion from your partner that you go to the cinema for a fun sedentary activity, then your level of control needs tapering down slightly. It's important to learn to be able to be flexible, enjoy being with others and not need to always know or control what will happen when or what will be eaten, learning to enjoy spontaneity. For some though, the opposite of being overly controlling is true and where that's the case, it's time to take on more decisive action and a little more control. When you can't trust your food choices, look to others to make most of your decisions for you or seek permission from someone else to do the things that you know you need to do, then it's time to grab hold of your empowerment and allow your brain to reprogram with some decisive and proud action.

Confirmation Bias

Your brain will have a strong bias when you have a restrictive eating disorder that will effectively be putting blinkers on you so that you are not as capable of noticing all the foods that you could be eating, all the people who live in very healthy bodies with big appetites and who don't spend all day compensating for it or the incredible life you could have if the eating disorder wasn't part of it. As you work to bash the eating disorder out of your life, it's time to open your eyes to the reality of the world. Notice how many food options you have, all the people in the world who eat and rest well and aren't dying of *obesity*-related conditions and the life opportunities you could pursue if you open your mind to them.

Tummy Troubles

When your tummy has only been used to restrictive amounts and food types for some years and repairing damage to your weakened stomach and intestines is low down your body's priority list because your heart and lungs take precedence, tummy troubles are an inevitable part of overcoming an eating disorder. The risk arises when you don't recognise them as inevitable—something that's happening because your stomach is learning to process different foods again, build strength and the necessary digestive enzymes and gut bacteria—and instead, you seek a reason for the bloating, constipation, diarrhoea and pain. This is when people commonly decide to cut out food groups, declaring an intolerance or reduce the amount they are eating. But doing so leads to dangerous territory—that of further unnecessary and damaging restriction—and it does little to help your belly heal in the long term. So, it's time to stock up on antacids and antispasmodics, grab a hot water bottle, let yourself relax, give your stomach a massage and eat all the foods you have avoided so that your stomach becomes strong and healthy with all the enzymes and good bacteria you need to be able to process any foods in future.

Blaming Others for Lack of Support

Yep, I'm sure we've all been there. Get mad with a loved one for being unsupportive or just for breathing and use that as a reason to not eat more today and it's their fault, not yours! Your brain will try every trick to stop you from making changes that take you away from your habits and addictive pursuit of energy deficit. The irritability with or blame of loved ones or other people in your life, including professionals or coaches, is a common pitfall. At the end of the day though, when this happens, the person it hurts the most is you because you hold onto the eating disorder yet another day. This then takes us back to the advice about self-empowerment and owning your process.

Thinking You Can Run Before You Can Walk

I appreciate this title is perhaps not the best in a book where many readers have compulsive running and walking habits but you know I'm speaking metaphorically (I hope)! This little metaphor is when you think to yourself that you have been doing this recovery thing for x amount of time now and should be done with it. You have gained a bit of weight and you can eat more so it's time to just get on with life. But you are not there yet. Your body still hasn't come out of energy deficit, despite some weight gain. Your brain still has reprogramming work to do and as frustrating as it is, this process will take longer. So, when you have thoughts that, *Surely I shouldn't be this hungry anymore*, rather than deny your ongoing high hunger, respect and honour it. When you are at the end of this process, you won't keep questioning it and the frustration will subside because your brain will have reprogrammed and your body will be at the point needed for your optimal health.

Focusing on Your Weight & Obsessing About Overshoot

Yep, the book is called *Aiming for Overshoot* because I want you to under-stand how important overshoot is to ensure you do fully emerge from energy deficit. By actively aiming for it, you are more likely to engage in the necessary abstinence from all the behaviours pursuing energy deficit you might have, so your brain also has the best chance of reprogramming. But overly focusing on your weight and overshoot is a pitfall too many fall into. People become obsessed with focusing on their weight gain, questioning if they are in overshoot now, when will the overshoot weight come down and whether they should be eating less or doing anything to make it happen. These questions and this anxiety only maintain the restrictive and eating disordered mindset, which can result in unconsciously returning to behaviours that pursue energy deficit, looking to get the overshoot weight off. But no one can tell you when your body is in overshoot and when it's not. Your body knows what it's doing and you need to keep eating, let the focus on your weight go and get on with enjoying your life instead. Choose to accept your body at any size it needs to be and let it decide what that is.

Pushing Out the Walls of Your *Feck No* Zone but Not Removing Them

This risk was covered in more detail in Chapter 45 which is all about the *Feck No!* zone. Your safety zone grows with how much you can eat, rest or not engage in other behaviours but despite this, there are still big walls stopping you going further. Your addiction to energy deficit and the behaviours are still powerful, impacting your ability to live freely, it's just that your brain now gets its hit from these new limits. You know what's needed here... charge into your *Feck No* zone!

Side Steps Rather Than Forward Ones

You convince yourself and those around you that you are making changes but they are really a side rather than a forward step because the forward steps are where the resistance lies and a side step just feels easier. An example of this is deciding you will tackle a *fear food* rather than eat more because eating something that you haven't for a while that is of similar energy value to your *safe* foods feels more comfortable and allows you to hold onto the same level of energy deficit. Or you don't purge by vomiting but avoid doing so by taking the dog for a walk—hmmm... see what happened there? Ensure you are taking big steps forwards and not allowing your brain to negotiate and find other ways to get its dopamine hit by convincing you that you are still making a meaningful change when that might not be the case. Big changes are always better!

Chapter 75

The Best Things About an Eating Disorder-Free Life

Much of the information in this book has included *warnings* about how hard overcoming an eating disorder is, the life changes you might need to make and the level of focus and challenge it will demand. This is because to be forewarned is to be forearmed. And let's face it, if overcoming a restrictive eating disorder were easy, you wouldn't be reading this book. You would have made a quick trip to McDonalds one day, eaten a couple of Mars bars the next and be done. Sadly, it's not that simple. You have some hard work ahead to get the eating disorder out of your life. But is it really worth putting yourself through all the pain and hard work?

It's time to explore the best things about an eating disorder-free life and why the pain and hard work might just be worth it.

An Eating Disorder-Free Life Can Bring:

- A life that is richer in all ways—more colour, richer experiences, the ability to smile and feel free.

- Not being hungry because when you are, you eat, with no more thought than that.

- No longer eating only to the clock.

- Mental freedom without constant food thoughts, calculations about when you will engage in compulsions or other mental gymnastics.

- Days without a groundhog sense to them.

- The ability to be you—the real you. The journey of self-discovery you will have will ensure that you connect to your authentic self in a way that feels incredible.

- Letting yourself change in positive ways, not being afraid of change and trusting it will all work out.

- The ability to not care one iota about what a number on a scale says because it doesn't define you.

- A better relationship with your body and your shape and size than most people in today's diet culture ever achieve.

- Better relationships with your loved ones, friends, colleagues, pets and anyone else.

- No longer being a worry and concern to your loved ones.

- A return of your libido if it was lost.

- A return of your periods if they were lost (for females).

- A return of your ability to have and sustain erections and full sperm motility if that was lost (for males).

- Laughing again.

- Crying again.

- Not feeling so anxious all the time.

- Less depression, thoughts of self-harm or suicide.

- Generally feeling much more positive in your daily life and outlook.

- Smiling more.

- Feeling that you can let the masks you have worn for years slip because you no longer need them.

- A life that makes sense.

- More time—no longer being driven to engage in pointless compulsions and rituals frees up mental space, physical energy and so much time.

- The ability to spend money and not be constrained by not letting yourself spend when you can afford to.

- A life you want to live, not living by *shoulds* or trying to please other people or an eating disorder.

- A certainty that you can make plans for your future in big ways and they won't be made impossible or tainted by an eating disorder.

- Having focus and concentration for the things that matter.

- Being able to live fully by your values, not the values of an eating disorder.

- More self-belief, self-awareness, gratitude, strength and ability to be vulnerable than most people ever gain.

- Consistently better sleep.

- Much better digestion.

- Feeling warm.

- More empathy for others, less judgment and prejudices.

- Freedom!

I could keep writing this list for a very long time. In fact, it could be a book in itself but as I'm already conscious that this book is getting very long and that you probably need to get more food, I'll end the list there. Suffice to say, an eating disorder-free life rocks and truth be told, it rocks even more because you have had the experience of living with an eating disorder. This means that for you, the small pleasures in life, such as being able to put your feet up in the afternoon with a cuppa and a large slab of cake, with no overthinking, anxiety or guilt, won't be something you will ever take for granted.

The work to gain your freedom is worth it. It's more than worth it so please keep going, using all the tools, support and time you need to find your free life and discover who you are without an eating disorder. Take the time now to do the work. It will be worth it for the sake of the rest of your life.

Chapter 76

Final Tips

This book has given you a lot of information, advice and guidance on how to navigate the challenges of overcoming a restrictive eating disorder and if you want more, you will find it in *Addicted to Energy Deficit*. Before I put my pen (or keyboard) down and leave you to your happy pursuit of overshoot, I will give you some final tips to ensure you are as armed as possible to completely bash the eating disorder from your life.

1. Change Everything Possible

The importance of changing as much of your routine, environment and day-to-day life as possible so that you avoid the cues, triggers and rituals that activate the eating disorder neural network has been covered repeatedly. Once your brain starts following the eating disorder's habitual pathways, it becomes much harder to put the brakes on and stop yourself. Therefore, addressing the cues that lead to the full habit through changes to your environment and life can make it much easier to implement the necessary abstinence approach.

2. Shake Everything Up Regularly

Avoid getting stuck in new routines and habits that only create a new safety zone in which the eating disorder and its addictive pursuit are ultimately still in control. Regularly shake up your routine, the foods you are eating, where and when you eat, how you spend your time, where you go and what you do until you are well beyond your *Feck No* zone!

3. Make Big Changes At Once

One final time of saying this—big changes and doing it all together might seem on the surface to be the more terrifying option but it's often the easiest when you do it. It also gives you the best chance of effective and lasting brain reprogramming because you build completely separate brain circuits to your entrenched eating disorder neural network. Big changes also ensure you are heading for overshoot and successful physical restoration, meaning you fully emerge from energy deficit before you burn out or have time to become too anxious about the weight changes.

4. Enjoy the Process

The more enjoyment, fun, positivity and general good times you can find during the process, the higher the likelihood that your brain will wire in these new changes as great things worth repeating. Yes, at times it's tough, but you are allowed to enjoy yourself and feel proud as you overcome the eating disorder and you should.

5. Identity

Tune into your gut instincts and your authentic self—the you who has likely been suppressed for years. Start to say yes to the real you, rather than please the eating disorder or others. And let the eating disorder identity go, as you discover who you really are, developing a new, strong identity that you feel truly connected to.

6. Take Time Out Now For the Sake of the Rest of Your Life

Just saying...

7. Food Should be Pleasurable!

People often say, *I really love food*, as if it's a dirty secret they are carrying around with them and something to be ashamed of. Pleasure from food is normal. It's an evolved survival response. Humans and animals need to derive pleasure from food so they are motivated to continue to eat and the species doesn't die out from hunger. You don't lose these evolved pleasure circuits that light up when you eat just because you have a restrictive eating disorder. You just developed conflicting circuits that drive an addictive aversion response to eating. Overcoming an eating disorder means allowing yourself to now stop responding to the aversion response, and start to pursue all the pleasures that come from eating and being satiated, with no shame, only pride.

8. Self-Awareness & Ongoing Reflection

You will need to develop excellent self-awareness skills so you can recognise what your brain is doing at any particular moment to stop yourself from following the automatic eating disorder pathways and deliberately pursue new ones. It's critical to be able to recognise habitual thoughts, self-talk, limiting beliefs and patterns of emotion that all act as triggers to your old habits so you can change your response. You need to notice when you are displaying non-physical signs of hunger and respond, no matter how clunky it feels, as well as identify when you are engaging in behaviours that to others might seem ok, even applaudable, but you know are driven by the eating disorder. In developing this insight and reflective practices, you can ensure that you continue to make progress.

9. Treat Your Body as a Vulnerable Child or Creature

If you had been left as the sole carer of a vulnerable child or creature and it was semi-starved and hungry, what would you do? Feed it, nurture it, keep it warm and wrapped up? You are the sole carer for your body, it doesn't have anyone else. Treat it as you would anything else that's vulnerable in your care. Feed and nurture it and allow it to rest and be warm so it can heal and grow[1].

10. Recognise the Stories Your Brain Creates to Keep You Stuck

Everyone has real and powerful stories that have formed into beliefs that allow them to rationalise to themselves and/or others why they are as driven as they are to keep pursuing these self-starvation habits. For many, the fear of weight gain story is the biggest driver. If that's you then I know it's real and powerful to you and reinforced by our culture. For others, the stories stem from painful memories or trauma, difficult relationships, a phobia of vomiting or a belief they will only be happy if they can continue to run xx miles a day. All these stories and beliefs, despite feeling credible, are not the reason you are trapped with an eating disorder. You are addicted to energy deficit and the dopamine hit it creates. Once you can overcome that addiction, you will realise that you weren't ever as bothered about weight gain as you believed, you are better able to manage past trauma or difficult memories and relationships when you have more brain space and emotional resilience to do so and you really don't like running that much at all! The stories that keep you stuck feel real and powerful and you believe them because they have kept you in the numb and seemingly safe eating disorder bubble for years. But now you need to recognise the stories, change your narrative and move past them, using therapy or support to manage any arising trauma or challenging emotions as you do so.

11. Reassure Yourself that the Difficult Emotions & Withdrawal Symptoms are Normal

More information was provided in *Addicted to Energy Deficit* about why you experience the challenging withdrawal symptoms, including negative emotions, such as anxiety, fear, agitation and low mood and physical effects such as headaches or poor sleep as you are overcoming the eating disorder. It's these very symptoms that have held you in the eating disorder all this time because as soon as a withdrawal effect sets in, your brain will quickly try to soothe it by pulling you back into another energy deficit-creating *fix*. When you abstain, the withdrawal symptoms can set in and they are uncomfortable and challenging. But remind yourself they are expected and normal. Your dopamine level is dropping to naturally rebalance and your brain is working hard to learn new ways of living. Pursuing old habits to soothe these symptoms will only make them worse in the longer term so reassure yourself that you are safe, you can tolerate them and it will be worth it.

12. Stop Negotiating with the Eating Disorder

Notice when you are letting yourself negotiate with the eating disorder. This can manifest as, *Well ok, I've eaten more today so perhaps it's ok to not push more; I won't go for a run but perhaps I'll just take the dog for a long walk; I haven't purged through vomiting today but I better not eat any more to be safe; I'll eat the bigger breakfast now but lunch can be smaller..* and on and on it goes. Constant mental gymnastics and negotiations keep you trapped. Let it all go. When you notice the negotiations set in, no matter how persuasive they are, stop negotiating and take determined action towards abstinence and your freedom.

13. Apply Curiosity & Approach The Process as an Experiment

A mindset that helped me as I worked to overcome the eating disorder was to view the process as an experiment, being curious as to what it would bring. View your process to abstain and aim for overshoot as an experiment you are taking on. You will wait for the results with interest and review your next steps at that time.

14. Everyday Matters—Make Every Day More

Cut back on your intake or use compensatory behaviours a bit more one day and it gives your brain an extra taste of its *drug*, sparking cravings for more the next. It then feels impossible to eat more than you did the day before or engage less in compensatory behaviours, despite having been doing so much better just two days previously. Be aware of the risks just one bad day brings with it. Every day matters. Focus on making every day a day of full abstinence and no going back. You can't afford to take days off in this process or to only make changes on the days you *feel like it.* It's tough but do it anyway.

15. Apply the See-Saw Analogy to the Pursuit of Energy Deficit

The see-saw analogy about restoring dopamine levels to a level balance has been used already. Apply it now also to the pursuit of energy deficit. You have pulled yourself into the depths of energy deficit for a long time—being hungry, using compulsive behaviours, staying constantly on the go, and leaving your body in a state of semi-starvation and exhaustion. When you let go of all these things, the need to eat and rest can rapidly swing in the opposite direction as the hunger, exhaustion and feeling that you are done with the eating disorder strikes. This is your energy deficit seesaw swinging the other way to pursue the energy surplus it needs to eventually restore balance. Let yourself swing to the other side and rest, eat and restore, allowing your seesaw to gradually creep to a level balance, where you can eat to *normal* hunger levels, rest when you need and lose the urge to always be on the go in destructive ways.

16. Remember that the Toughest Days are the Most Critical

The days that you want to give up, when the emotions are strong, your body image low and all you want to do is crawl into a safe and numb-feeling eating disorder bubble are the days that are the most important to stay committed to overcoming the eating disorder. In fact, if you can take big steps forward on days like this, when it feels the most impossible, the brain reprogramming that comes from it will be significant. Changing your automatic response to hard days, negative emotions or stress from one driven by the eating disorder into something eating disorder-bashing will ensure that your brain notices and the eating disorder network that was its go-to when times were tough will become less of an automatic response. This is when your brain learns that there are alternative ways to respond to stress. Of course, changing your automatic response when you feel low and uncomfortable into one that then creates further anxiety and agitation is not easy. But it's tolerating discomfort in the short term for the sake of a brain in the future that stops trying to lure you back to the eating disorder on an *ugh* day.

17. Don't Compare Your Journey to Someone Else's

Just don't. It never helps. Every journey is different and everyone has a different history and life circumstances. And you only see what's on the outside—you have no idea what's happening within them. Compare leads to despair so focus on your journey and what you know is right for your progress.

18. Use Resistance as Your Internal Sat-Nav

Where resistance lies I must travel...
I'm not sure if that's a quote or if I just made it up, but ultimately internal resistance in the shape of automatic thoughts, limiting beliefs, anxiety, fear responses or just a deeply felt knowledge that you shouldn't take the positive, eating disorder-bashing action right now is your internal satnav for the direction you need to take. Anything that creates discomfort is likely to be the very thing that will reprogram your brain and lead you out of energy deficit. Allow resistance to show you the way.

19. Step into the *Feck No!* Zone & Truly Aim for Overshoot

I think this sums it all up.

---

1. Taken from a talk with Gabor Mate.

Chapter 77

That's All Folks — Concluding with Clare's Words

*A*iming for Overshoot has covered a lot of hints, tips, advice and information to help you navigate the often challenging but ultimately positive process of overcoming a restrictive eating disorder, all written by my (now) tired fingers. Therefore, to bring these pages to a fitting conclusion, I thought I'd let a very inspiring client share her first-hand experiences and overall message with you.

Clare is a woman in her fifties who lived with a restrictive eating disorder for over a decade. She had started working with me to overcome it just four months before she wrote the words below. When Clare started her eating disorder-bashing journey, she was eating a restrictive vegan diet and was an extreme runner, often running 100 miles a week or more in truly addictive ways. In our first contact, Clare described herself as identifying strongly with being *a runner* and she couldn't conceive of this not being part of her future, but she was willing to keep an open mind.

Clare jumped into the process of intensive abstinence from her eating disorder behaviours from day one. She stopped running and any other forms of movement or exercise beyond what was absolutely necessary for daily life. She embraced eating more, responding to her hunger in all its forms. In doing so, she gained weight, increasing several clothes sizes. At first, this wasn't comfortable for her but with only a few wobbles, she accepted the changes with positivity and even intrigue at times. Clare adopted a mindset, of *I'm doing this and will do whatever it takes,* which is perhaps why she made the progress she did in such a short time.

In just four months, Clare transformed in ways that were inspiring to see and I felt honoured to be a support and cheerleader on her journey. I asked Clare to share what advice she would give to someone beginning the process today or who was in the thick of it—her response summed up all I could have said and more. I hope you find this helpful:

Clare's Words:

I could write an essay on my advice to someone starting on their recovery journey. There's so much to say.

The most important thing for me was that I had to want to recover, not have someone else tell me to do so. Liz (Clare's partner) tried over and over again to get me to seek help but I had to be in the right place to do it, and to me, that meant mentally, physically (I was running noticeably slower) and geographically. Of course, many people don't have a choice and recovery is forced on them. The thought of ending up in hospital terrified me and was a big factor in getting help when I did.

So my advice based on my experience is:

1. *Don't listen to anyone, or yourself, who tells you that you can't recover. You can and you will if you stick with it and bash away at the eating disorder every moment of every day.*

2. *Don't do it on your own. You need support from someone who knows what they are talking about and who understands what you are going through. Choose wisely. My first dabble with recovery did more harm than good. You need someone who offers the type and level of support you want. I knew I needed regular and very practical support based on fact, not theory. I didn't want someone to psychoanalyse and look at my past. I wanted someone to guide me every day with what to do and what not to do. I needed someone firm but kind, someone to push me and also to pick me up when things were a bit shit (*apparently I met the criteria for this*).*

3. *Get the rest of your support team on board, which in my case has been Liz. Her support has been crucial. Talk openly to the person or people who are supporting you too so that they can understand how best to help, and remember that your recovery process will be a confusing and difficult time for them too.*

4. *Invest in the process. It takes a lot of energy so don't expect to carry on with your life as normal. If you can afford to stop work and focus on nothing else then do so. Spend time each day reflecting, being very honest with yourself about what's going well, what hasn't gone so well and what needs to change. Take time to notice the changes taking place in you and your life and celebrate each little (or big) win. I shall always remember my first pasty* (I think they've been the theme of my recovery) and when Liz said she never knew I could be so relaxed and able to laugh.*

5. *Jump in with both feet. Recovery isn't a whole lot of fun, particularly in the early days, so you may as well go fast and get it over and done with as quickly as possible! But....*

6. *Recovery takes time. Be impatiently patient. I've wanted to recover as quickly as I can but I've recognised I can't speed up the processes I have no control over, such as body repair.*

7. *Don't assume it will all be horrendous. It's definitely hard but it doesn't have to be awful all of the time. Try and enjoy recovery, especially eating all the food you know deep down you love but have convinced yourself you don't. You never have to have that stomach-aching horrible hungry feeling again.*

8. *Enjoy rediscovering your old self. As much as you don't think you'll change, you will, and 100% for the better.*

9. *Put your determination to good use. I think everyone with an eating disorder must be very determined and strong-willed to eat so little, follow such set routines and exercise so compulsively.*

10. *Regardless of how good you are at your sport, you have to stop completely to recover. My trophies, medals, course record, etc were meaningless. I was ill and getting more and more so each day. If I hadn't stopped running (and everything else) on day one I'd have gotten nowhere.*

11. *Don't dwell on the past and regret what you did or didn't do. Leave it in the past, move on and look forward to an exciting future. But.....*

12. *Don't look too far into the future. Small steps and one day at a time, particularly in the early days. Don't catastrophise (as I did quite often).*

13. *Never, ever try on your old clothes. Get rid of them immediately and buy things that make you feel comfortable and happy and have lots of growing room. Definitely buy baggy dungarees (*Clare is a queen of great dungarees and proudly wears them!*).*

14. *Be positive. I've tried to stay as positive as I can throughout the process and it has been a massive help to me. Some days it was a struggle but even on*

my lowest days, I always found something to feel positive about.

15. *Go for it! An (almost) eating disorder-free life is the best (*Clare puts 'almost' in this sentence because she isn't quite eating disorder-free yet but she will be very soon).

I could go on and on with more advice but I will stop there.

Overall, I feel very, very fortunate to have reached where I am today in just four months. I'm not sure I truly believed it was possible and definitely not that I could happily spend a day eating lots of cake and pasties while sitting on the sofa!

*For any readers not from Cornwall or the UK, a pastie is a delicious filled pastry that originates from Cornwall and that Clare has embraced a passion for since deciding to fully abstain from all restriction.

A big thank you to Clare for sharing this. First-hand advice from someone who has been there recently can make a big difference and so I hope that Clare's message inspires you and offers you hope.

And with that, all that's left for me to say is thank you for reading these pages. But most of all, believe you can do this. I know you can and if you believe you can, seek the right support, don't try to go it alone and embrace the process in all ways possible, you will find your unique path to your unique future. I guarantee, whatever your future brings, it will be easier and happier without a restrictive eating disorder shadowing it.

Keep aiming for overshoot and be fabulous!

Helly x

About the Author

Helly Barnes is a professional coach for people overcoming restrictive eating disorders. She uses neuroscience, research, her personal history with an eating disorder and her professional experience to provide an informed approach and empower anyone to overcome the destructive and addictive nature of an eating disorder.

Helly now lives an unconventional life, following her heart. She considers herself a full-time nomad and she is never happier than when travelling the world and appreciating all it has to offer.

Useful Links to the Author

While in the process of overcoming a 14-year-history of a restrictive eating disorder, Helly kept a blog of her experiences still available at:

www.recoveringnomad.com

And Helly writes a regular blog today on her coaching website:

www.hellybarnes.com

You will also find more information and ramblings by Helly on her podcast series,

Feck it, Fun, Fabulous and Free in Eating Disorder Recovery,

which is freely available on all mainstream podcasting platforms.

Addicted to Energy Deficit

M y first book, *Addicted to Energy Deficit*, is also available to buy now from online book retailers both as an e-book or in paperback:

When a restrictive eating disorder has had a destructive effect on your life or the life of someone you care about and you haven't been able to understand why it's so hard to overcome, Addicted to Energy Deficit is the book you need.

Bringing in neuroscience and research evidence, as well as personal and professional experience, Helly Barnes provides an explanation for restrictive eating disorders that will resolve your unanswered questions and fit your experience.
This includes:

- *A credible explanation for restrictive eating disorders as a brain-based addiction to the state of energy deficit.*

- *The evolutionary, genetic and external factors that made you susceptible.*

- *The most effective methods to overcome the addictive pursuit of energy deficit.*

- *How to reprogram your brain through processes of deep learning and dopamine restoration.*

- *Why self-empowerment, support and connection are critical.*

- *The cause of extreme levels of hunger and why you need to respond to them.*

- *The importance of set point theory and fat overshoot.*

- *Why you are not as afraid of weight gain as you think.*

- *How to avoid relapse WHEN you find your free future.*

This informative and compassionate guide will give you a deeper understanding of yourself and the eating disorder. You will believe that you can overcome it and feel empowered to take the necessary steps to do so.

Made in the USA
Middletown, DE
07 August 2024

58690711R00232